GRAMMAR SKILLS

Grades 6–8

by Rosemary Allen

Published by World Teachers Press®

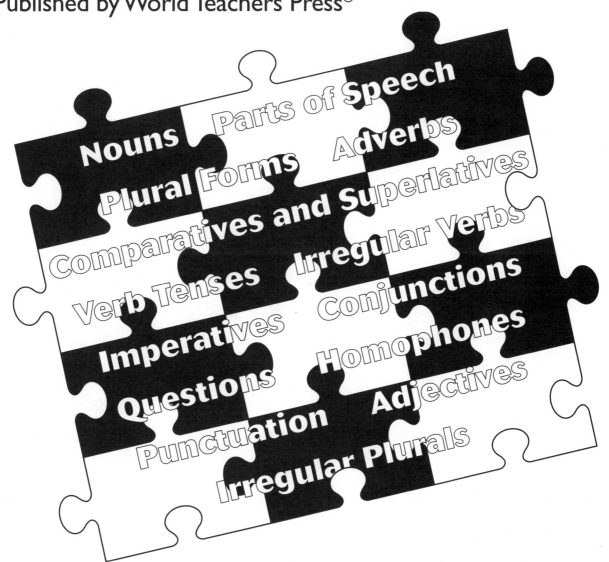

Nouns Parts of Speech Adverbs
Plural Forms
Comparatives and Superlatives
Verb Tenses Irregular Verbs
Imperatives Conjunctions
Questions Homophones
Punctuation Adjectives
Irregular Plurals

Order Number 2-5129
ISBN 1-58324-053-5

C D E F G 06 05 04 03

Educational Resources
395 Main Street
Rowley, MA 01969
www.worldteacherspress.com

Over the years, controversy about the value of teaching grammar concepts to students has challenged teachers and, to some degree, led to an uncertainty in this area of the curriculum. However, there has been a resurgence of interest in grammar and a recognition of the need for teachers and students to share a common language which allows them to talk *about* language and how it operates as a resource for making meaning.

This three book series has been written in response to this need: to provide you with a practical teaching resource that can add to your knowledge of how the English language functions and how it is organized to serve those functions. It recognizes that basic to any teacher's effort to help students improve their grammar is the teacher's own understanding of how the English language works.

Students will work through a wide range of English grammar concepts, both in isolation, and in the context of text. Concepts are presented in a form that is easy to understand and pages contain explanation and a variety of activities.

Detailed teachers notes have been included on pages 6 and 7 and in the answer pages, providing explanations and extra activity ideas where appropriate.

Contents

Contents

Grammar Skills Teachers Notes

The central premise of *Grammar Skills* is that control over language cannot be viewed as a simple by-product of reading, writing, listening and speaking (although these are of prime importance for language and growth), but requires a more explicit knowledge developed by studying how grammar works in various situations. Therefore, a functional approach to English grammar has been adopted for this series.

Grammar Skills explores, in context, the systematic relationship between the features of English grammar. It seems that too often in teaching we become so involved in the parts, we forget to relate them back to the whole: we drill students on the components and then deny them the opportunity to see how the subparts combine to form an integral and meaningful whole. Building on this base of understanding, deliberate measures can then be taken

to reinforce and practice the use of those parts. The main aim is to help students progressively gain control over grammar by studying the way it works in real and various situations.

One book, however, cannot be a panacea. In addition, you will need to support and extend the concepts introduced in *Grammar Skills* through a variety of activities using resources and strategies such as: language experience, shared book experiences, problem solving, sentence makers, cloze exercises, environmental print, modeled writing and games. You will need to constantly link forms and language conventions, within the demands that a particular writing situation creates, and allow students to reinforce and practice what they have discovered. In this way you will be taking deliberate measures to improve your students' ability to handle language.

Teachers Notes and Answers

At the back of each book in the English Grammar series are detailed teachers notes and answers. These notes provide background information on the specific grammar concepts being studied and answers where required.

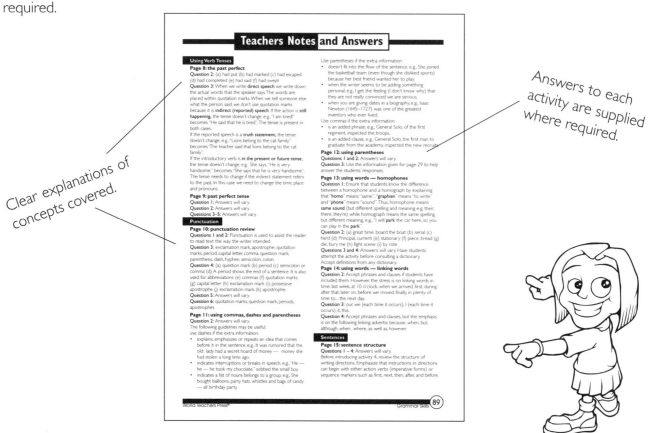

Clear explanations of concepts covered.

Answers to each activity are supplied where required.

Grammar Skills | Teachers Notes

Activity Pages

Each activity page develops a specific English grammar concept. "Did You Know" sections provide clear explanations in terms suitable for easy comprehension. Students are often asked to provide explanation of the concepts in their own words to ascertain the level of understanding. Activities are clearly laid out and require concise answers, with a level of repetition to ensure understanding.

Title: explains the general grammar area.

Subtitle: explains the specific concept being treated.

"Did you know?" sections provide students with a clear and helpful explanation of different aspects of the concept being treated.

Students are often required to show an understanding of the concept when completing activities.

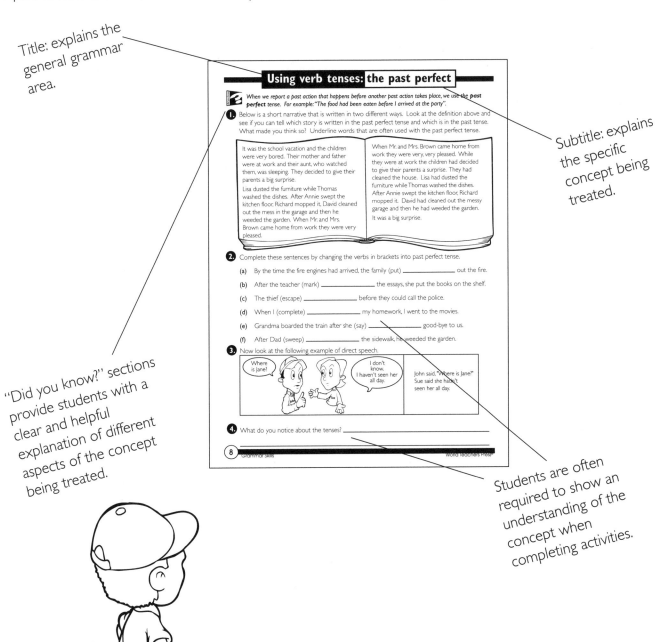

Using verb tenses: the past perfect

*When we report a past action that happens before another past action takes place, we use the **past perfect** tense. For example: "The food had been eaten before I arrived at the party."*

1. Below is a short narrative that is written in two different ways. Look at the definition above and see if you can tell which story is written in the past perfect tense and which is in the past tense. What made you think so? Underline words that are often used with the past perfect tense.

It was the school vacation and the children were very bored. Their mother and father were at work and their aunt, who watched them, was sleeping. They decided to give their parents a big surprise.

Lisa dusted the furniture while Thomas washed the dishes. After Annie swept the kitchen floor, Richard mopped it, David cleaned out the mess in the garage and then he weeded the garden. When Mr. and Mrs. Brown came home from work they were very pleased.

When Mr. and Mrs. Brown came home from work they were very, very pleased. While they were at work the children had decided to give their parents a surprise. They had cleaned the house. Lisa had dusted the furniture while Thomas washed the dishes. After Annie swept the kitchen floor, Richard mopped it. David had cleaned out the messy garage and then he had weeded the garden.

It was a big surprise.

2. Complete these sentences by changing the verbs in parentheses into past perfect tense.

(a) By the time the fire engines had arrived, the family (put) _____ out the fire.

(b) After the teacher (mark) _____ the essays, she put the books on the shelf.

(c) The thief (escape) _____ before they could call the police.

(d) When I (complete) _____ my homework, I went to the movies.

(e) Grandma boarded the train after she (say) _____ good-bye to us.

(f) After Dad (sweep) _____ the sidewalk, he weeded the garden.

3. Now look at the following example of direct speech.

4. What do you notice about the tenses? _____

_____

More about the past perfect tense

1. Here is a chart of sentence parts. Use it to make twelve sentences and write them on another piece of paper. Work on your own and then compare your sentences with those of the other members in your group. Discuss which sentences make sense and those which do not.

2. How can you tell the sentences you have made are written in the past perfect tense?

_____

_____

3. Use past perfect tense to write three sentences about when you were six years old. For example, **I had lost two teeth by the time I was six years old.**

(a) _____

(b) _____

(c) _____

4. Write three examples of how the past perfect is used in indirect speech. For example, **He said, "I have already completed the task."** becomes **"He said he had already completed the task."**

(a) _____

_____

(b) _____

_____

(c) _____

_____

5. Examine some newspaper articles. Find examples of indirect (reported) speech. Is the reported speech written in the past perfect tense? Is there any direct speech in the articles? In which tense is the direct speech written? Write your answers on another piece of paper.

Using punctuation: review

1. Do you think that **punctuation** is important? ☐ Yes ☐ No

2. Explain your answer. _____

_____

_____

3. Name some of the most common punctuation marks. _____

_____

_____

4. Look at the table below. Complete it by naming the punctuation mark(s) next to the reason given for using it.

Reasons for using punctuation marks		Marks to use
(a)	to show a question is being asked	
(b)	to mark the end of a sentence	
(c)	to show a short space in reading	
(d)	to mark abbreviations	
(e)	to separate items in a list	
(f)	to show the words someone is saying	
(g)	to show the word is a proper noun	
(h)	to show an order is given	
(i)	to show ownership	
(j)	to show surprise or sudden comment	
(k)	to show some letters have been left out	

5. Now write sentences of your own on another piece of paper. Show each of these punctuation marks. You may have up to ten sentences.

6. Use the table above to help you list the punctuation marks used in the following sentence.
"Have you seen the new movie yet?" asked Tom.
"It's a good movie. I've seen it three times already."

_____

_____

World Teachers Press®

Commas, dashes and parentheses

Sometimes when you write a sentence, you want to make the meaning clearer by adding some information. You can do this in a number of ways.

1. Look at these sentence pairs. Check the one that gives the most information.

(a) ☐ My uncle loves to visit me.

☐ My uncle — the one who lives alone — loves to visit me.

(b) ☐ I get the feeling (I don't know why) that you are not listening to me.

☐ I get the feeling you are not listening to me.

(c) ☐ There is a very good reason why we have school rules — to guide student behavior.

☐ There is a very good reason why we have school rules.

(d) ☐ The wolf, trying to hide in the shadows, followed Red Riding Hood through the woods.

☐ The wolf followed Red Riding Hood through the woods.

(e) ☐ My aunt gave me a kitten (I don't really like cats) for my birthday.

☐ My aunt gave me a kitten for my birthday.

(f) ☐ He looked at the monster.

☐ He looked at the monster — the monster who had saved his life.

(g) ☐ We searched the beach — every inlet, every bay and every cove — but the diamond was nowhere to be found.

☐ We searched the beach, but the diamond was nowhere to be found.

(h) ☐ He chose his friend John to play on his team.

☐ He chose his friend John (although he could have chosen a better player) to play on his team.

2. Examine the sentences with the most information. Look at the different punctuation marks that have been used. Write your own sentences below using the different types of punctuation.

_____

_____

_____

_____

_____

More about parenthetical expressions

The names of three kinds of punctuation that helped to add information to sentences were: parentheses, commas and dashes. You may like to try these in your own writing first, as you need to understand when to use each of them. Your teacher will tell you some simple rules to help you.

1. Now add extra information to these sentences to help make the meaning clearer.

(a) She had beautiful things, but she was not happy. _____

_____

(b) A man offered me some help. _____

_____

(c) There were all kinds of people at the parade. _____

_____

(d) For the last three years we have lived in the old shack. _____

_____

(e) The three bears discovered Goldilocks asleep in Baby Bear's bed. _____

_____

(f) We arrived as quickly as we could. _____

_____

(g) My aunt is coming for a vacation. _____

_____

2. Read this short recipe that John wrote for his parents.

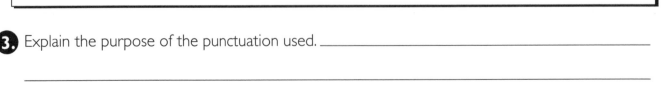

How to Make Your Child's Favorite Lunch

- Take a bread roll — the crunchy, wholewheat kind from the bakery — slice it in half and butter it on both sides.
- Slice tomatoes (thickly) and add them to the roll.
- Add a slice of cheese.
- Chop a sweet pickle — don't use the sour kind — and place it on top of the cheese.
- Finally, add the ham (two slices would be better than one) and cut the roll in half.
- Serve with a delicious vanilla milkshake — with bananas and honey in it. Yum!

3. Explain the purpose of the punctuation used. _____

_____

_____

Using words: homophones

1. Below are two sentences which have **homophones** written in bold print. Read them and write what you think a homophone is.

   (a) I don't know **whether** the **weather** will change today, so I'll take my umbrella in case.

   (b) I had to **wait** while she checked her **weight**.

_____

_____

2. Here are some sentences with homophones. Identify those that are incorrect and write them correctly on another piece of paper.

   (a) We had a grate time on bored the boat that traveled to the Isle of Capri.

   (b) We watched the cereal on TV at our friend's house and then we caught the bus.

   (c) The horse was bred at the stables but he escaped and joined a heard of wild horses in the mountains.

   (d) The Principle called a meeting of the school board to discuss the currant problems.

   (e) The train was stationery on the platform and the conductor called for them to board.

   (f) Please pass me the jam to spread on my peace of bred.

   (g) When I dye please berry me under the berry tree.

   (h) Have you seen the chase seen in the new movie?

   (i) She learned the points by wrote and then wrote them down for her friend.

3. Identify the meanings of the following homophones. Write sentences to clearly show the meaning of at least six of the words.

flour/flower
pause/paws
aloud/allowed
idol/idle
you/ewe
pair/pear

_____

_____

_____

_____

_____

_____

_____

_____

_____

4. On another piece of paper, see if you can write five sentences that include more than one of the same homophone, e.g., The builders are sealing the ceiling tiles with waterproof glue.

Making use of words: linking words

There are ways to link ideas in a sentence. Sometimes we link using words that tell about sequence and time. Sometimes we use pronouns to link ideas. Sometimes we use conjunctions.

1. Read this story written by a girl in fifth grade.

A Trip to the War Museum

Last week our class visited the War Museum in the city.

We left school at 10 o'clock and traveled by bus to the City Station. From there we walked to the museum and looked at some historical buildings along the way. The streets were not very crowded because it was the middle of the week, so we could see everything easily.

When we arrived at the museum, the class was split into five different groups. Some of the class went out with chaperones, but I stayed with Miss Green. First we went to the hall of fame and looked at pictures of some people who did brave things during the war. Miss Green said they were heroes. After that, we had a look at a display of medals and uniforms. Although that part was quite boring, it got better when we went to where there were some models of people, as well as some photographs taken during the war. Later on, the class all met up again and had lunch, before we moved into a small theater to see a documentary about World War 11. Finally, we filled in some quiz sheets.

The walk back to the bus terminal seemed to take ages. We were all very tired from walking around the museum. However, we made it in plenty of time to catch the 2:30 p.m. bus back to school.

The next day I was surprised to find that I had learned such a lot about a war just by going on a field trip. I think this is a better way to learn than sitting in a classroom.

---

2. Draw a circle around all of the linking words that tell about sequence or time.

3. Draw a red line under all of the pronouns that help to link the ideas between sentences.

4. Draw a blue line under all of the adverbs that help to link ideas together.

5. Think of somewhere you have been recently and write a story of your own.
You will need to:
- include an orientation that tells when, what, where and why you went there;
- link all of the events using sequence or time words — use pronouns and adverbs; and
- write a concluding statement.

_____

_____

_____

_____

_____

_____

_____

Sentence structure

1. Do you like sandwiches?

Yes ☐   No ☐

You are probably asking, "What does this have to do with sentence structure?" Well, in some ways sentences can be compared to sandwiches.

2. Can you think of one way a sentence can be compared to a sandwich?

_____

Sandwiches have a basic structure and so do sentences. Sandwiches have components (ingredients) that we choose to put in them. So do sentences. When we put the components into a sandwich, the order we put them in does not always matter. The sandwich will look different, but mostly it will taste the same. It's the same with sentences — we can change the order of the components in a sentence and, although the sentence may look different, the meaning often remains the same. We can also join two sentences together, just like we can make a double-decker sandwich.

For example, when I want to make a ham and cheese sandwich, I first take the basic structure of the sandwich, that is, two slices of bread. Then I add some ham, some slices of cheese and some lettuce.

Notice that commas are placed between each item in the list, but I do not need a comma before the word "and."

3. Name some other components you might add to a ham and cheese sandwich.

4. Invent your own special double-decker sandwich by adding the components you choose to the basic structure (the slices of bread). Write the directions in the space below.

_____

_____

_____

_____

_____

Sentences are like sandwiches; they too have a basic structure. Sentences are made up of clauses (ideas, messages, thoughts). A clause is the basic structure that carries the message of the sentence. It must contain a verb or a verb group. Sentences can be made up of a single clause (idea, message or thought) or can be made by linking two or more clauses.

1. Find suitable verbs to complete these sentences.

(a)　Jay _____ football so he _____ every night.

(b)　Kate _____ a letter to her friend.

(c)　Brad _____ the door as he _____ outside.

2. Read this short narrative first and then we can look more closely at the clauses.

The Tree House

The children were on vacation for six weeks so they decided to build a tree house in the big, old mulberry tree in the back field. Dad was recruited to help, timber was located, tools and ropes were borrowed and nails were acquired from Dad's collection in the shed. The children set to work happily on their project.

The tree house took three weeks to complete. It was solid and roomy. Dad said it was the superstar of the tree house world. However, there was still something missing and the children were not completely happy with the result, so they went to Dad for some further advice.

"I know what the problem is," he remarked, disappearing into the spare bedroom. He returned a few minutes later with two pieces of material.

"You need curtains to make it feel like a home." The children laughed. Dad was right. Now they had a real home of their own, not just a tree house.

Most of the sentences in the narrative have more than one clause (thought) in them. However, there are some sentences that have only one clause.
The children set to work happily on their project.
The tree house took three weeks to complete.

3. Look at the text again. Find other examples of sentences with only one clause.

_____

_____

_____

_____

_____

Let's look at a sentence that contains more than one clause. Each different idea (clause) in the sentence is shown on a different line.

The children were on vacation for six weeks
so they decided to build a tree house in the big, old mulberry tree.

This sentence has two clauses. The second clause begins with the word "so" which is a conjunction (joining word). The word "so" makes the relationship between the clauses very clear. It tells you the reason the children decided to build a tree house was because they were on vacation. There are other ways you can show how clauses are related, but we will examine these at a later time.

1. Here is another sentence. It contains four ideas (clauses).
Can you separate the clauses? Write each clause on a separate line.

Dad was recruited to help, timber was located, tools and ropes borrowed and nails acquired from Dad's collection in the shed.

_____

_____

_____

_____

In this sentence only the last clause begins with a conjunction (joining word). The conjunction used here is "and." Did you notice that the clauses are like a list of things the children had to do? The conjunction "and" tells us that a number of things have been added together, so the clauses are separated by commas. Another interesting thing about the last two clauses is that the words "was" and "were" have been left out. They are not needed because they are understood by the reader.

2. Rewrite the last sentence below leaving out "was" and "were" where you feel they are not necessary.

> Our class decided to have a fair to raise money for needy people. There were many things we had to do before the fair. Other classes were asked to assist, parents were recruited to help, second-hand toys and clothes were collected, donations of canned foods were requested, cookies and cakes were baked, a raffle was organized and presents were wrapped as prizes.

_____

_____

_____

_____

Identifying the components of a clause

 *The **components** of a clause are words or groups of words. Each of the components has a purpose.*

1. Divide this sentence to show the three components. **The children set to work happily.**

(a) _____

This part of the sentence tells us who (or what) the participants are. It is the **naming part** of the sentence.

(b) _____

This part tells us what is happening. It is the **action part** of the sentence.

(c) _____

This part tells us more about the **situation**. It tells us things about the naming part, like how, why, when, where and what.

 *The components of the clause are: the naming part, the action part, and the situation part. In this sentence the **naming part** comes first. The **action part** is next and the **situation part** is last. You may know these as subject, verb and object. You can change the order of your components.*
The sentence above can be written like this:
Happily, the children set to work.

2. Has the meaning changed? _____

What is the order now? ☐ naming part   ☐ action part   ☐ situation part

3. Changing the order of the components of sentences can make your writing more interesting. Change the order of these sentence components.

(a) The dentist drilled the tooth carefully. _____

_____

(b) Quietly, the crocodile slid into the water. _____

_____

(c) Justine waited impatiently for the bus. _____

_____

(d) Kieran swam powerfully through the water. _____

_____

Changing the order of sentences

1. Here are some one-clause **sentences**. First, mark the components.
Naming part: **N**, Action part: **A**, and Situation part: **S**.
Rewrite the sentences by changing the order of the components. The first one is done for you.

        N   **A**   **S**
The noisy crow / flew / high towards the maple tree.

        S   **N**   **A**

(a) *High towards the maple tree / the noisy crow / flew*

(b) The towering mountain range loomed, gloomy and forbidding, over the village.

_____

(c) The scouts folded their tents without any instruction from their leader.

_____

(d) The house next to the big park is Robert's house.

_____

(e) The football game was postponed because of the cyclone.

_____

(f) The car was stopped by the police because the driver was speeding.

_____

(g) The moon crept silently and softly across the dark, dark sky.

_____

2. Did you notice that sentence **(g)** had two parts in the situation component?

What are they? how: _____ where: _____

> *You can split up the situation components and move only one of them, if you prefer. For example, you could write: **Silently and softly, the moon crept across the dark, dark sky**.*

3. Examine these situation components.
Do they tell: how? why? when? where? or what?

		how?	why?	when?	where?	what?
(a)	gloomy and forbidding over the village	☐	☐	☐	☐	☐
(b)	is Robert's house	☐	☐	☐	☐	☐
(c)	as they marched past the officer	☐	☐	☐	☐	☐
(d)	because of the cyclone	☐	☐	☐	☐	☐

Clause structure: the subject (noun groups)

Noun groups can be people, objects, places and even things you cannot see, like emotions.

1. Add three more nouns to each noun group in the box provided.

(a) **Common noun**: a general name shared by things that belong to the same group.

girl   pen   desk
kitten   country   car

_____

(b) **Proper noun**: the name of a particular person or thing. Proper nouns always have capital letters.

Swan River   September   Wednesday
Robert   *Treasure Island*

_____

(c) **Abstract noun**: the name of something you cannot see or touch, as a quality, a condition or an idea.

beauty   courage   wealth
envy   length

_____

(d) **Collective noun**: the name of a group of things that belong together.

library   herd   gaggle
bouquet   audience   flock

_____

Nouns can also be:

masculine or feminine,   **singular or plural,**   **compound,**

lion/lioness uncle/aunt prince/princess boy/girl	witch/witches mouse/mice potato/potatoes baby/babies key/keys	waterfall milkshake sunglasses playground rainbow

possessive,   **countable, or**   **uncountable.**

boy's/boys' Jane's fox's/foxes' women's Mrs. Jones'	baskets balloons dogs tables	gold furniture courage sugar
		Uncountable nouns are always singular. You can't use "a" or "an" with them.

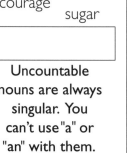

2. Add one more noun to each box above.

More about noun groups

1. Read the following story and underline all the nouns.

The Elephant Calf

Many years ago, before the deep jungles of Africa were trampled by people and machines, in a time when the Bongo River water was sweet and clean, an elephant calf was born. He was a beautiful elephant child and every member of the herd cherished him. They gave him advice and information in the hope that he would grow up strong and brave like his mother and father. He felt very safe and loved.

One day, during a torrential downpour, the little calf become separated from the herd. When the clouds drifted on and the sunshine peeped out, he was all alone. At first he wasn't worried, but as the day stretched on, he began to feel lonely and confused, so he plucked a bunch of ripe bananas and set out to look for someone to take care of him.

First he came upon a pride of lions. "Will you be my mother?" he asked a lioness, who was licking her paws and enjoying the sunshine. "That's impossible," she replied disdainfully. "We are the kings and queens of the jungle. Lionesses don't have calves, we have cubs. Go away and find yourself a calf mother."

Sadly, the little calf resumed his search. By and by he came across a flock of swans resting in the tall grass by the side of the river. "Will you be my mother?" he asked the nearest swan. "Don't be silly," said the female swan. "We have little cygnets to look after. We don't look after calves. Go away and find yourself a calf mother."

Just then, three big, grey shapes surfaced in the calm waters of the Bongo River. It was a herd of hippos. "Excuse me," said the elephant calf very politely. "Are you a calf mother, because if you are, will you be my calf mother?"

"Well!" gasped the hippo cow. She was quite taken aback. "My babies are calves and you seem like a nice fellow, but — like the giraffe and the water buffalo — I only look after my own kind of calf. You need an elephant cow to look after you. I'm sure I saw a herd of elephants downstream. Just follow the river to the bend and you'll see them too."

The little calf thanked her politely and continued the search for a calf mother of his own kind. It seemed a long time before he reached the bend in the river, but as he drew closer he could hear his mother's familiar trumpeting and the herd's splishing and splashing. He heard his aunts' and uncles' calls as they tried to guide him home. Hurrying around the bend, he knew he had found his family at last.

2. Name the animals in the story which have calves.

_____

_____

3. In the story the elephant calf comes across a flock of swans. Name three other types of animals that form flocks.

(a) _____

(b) _____

(c) _____

Clause components: nouns

1. See how many different types of nouns you can find in the story and list them under the correct heading below.

common nouns			proper nouns	abstract nouns
			pronouns	

collective nouns	compound nouns	possessive nouns

2. Check whether the nouns are M – masculine, F – feminine, S – singular, P – plural, C – countable or U – uncountable.

Noun	M	F	S	P	C	U
hippos						
cow						
flock						

Noun	M	F	S	P	C	U
water						
lion						
uncle						

World Teachers Press®

Clause structure: verbs (action part)

 The action components in a sentence are verbs. Verbs are sometimes called "doing words." They indicate if the action has happened, is happening or might happen in the future. Every sentence must have a verb. A verb on its own can be a sentence.

1. "**Look**! Dad's found my missing slipper."
Sentences like this are usually commands.

Think of another example.

_____

_____

2. Verbs can be a group of words.
He **has been playing** with his pet cat.

Think of another example.

_____

_____

3. Verbs can be a whole word.
The shop **sells** smoked salmon.

Think of another example.

_____

_____

4. Verbs can be part of a word.
"Mom, there**'s** a black cat in the kitchen."
"That**'s** all right, they**'re** lucky."

Think of another example.

_____

_____

 *Some verbs need helpers like: as, am, is, are, was, were, be, being, been, has, have, do, does and did, especially when the verb ends in "–ing." The helper verbs are called **auxiliaries**.*

5. "Why does the ocean always look so angry?"

Because it **has been crossed** so many times.

_____

_____

Clause structure: verbs

1. Can you find the verbs in this cartoon? Underline all the verbs you can find.

I'm looking for my skateboard. Where is it? It was here yesterday.

Sorry, I used it. I left it in the garage because Mom was calling me. Unfortunately, Dad ran over it with his car.

2. Write the verbs you found to show what types of verbs they are. Some might belong to more than one group.

Type of verb	Examples
part of a word	
groups of words	
action already happened	
have –ing at the end	

3. Underline the verbs in the sentences below.

(a) They arrived at the vet clinic and lifted the injured dog out of the car.

(b) In summer, the weather is hot, the days are longer and flies annoy you.

(c) The dressmaker alters and repairs clothes and designs special gowns.

(d) I'm going to the hairdresser first and then I'll pick you up.

(e) By six o'clock we will be in Chicago and then you can meet your aunt.

4. List four verbs from the sentences above and write the name of the group that describes the type of verb.

Verb	Type of verb
arrived	*action has already happened*

Words: using interesting verbs

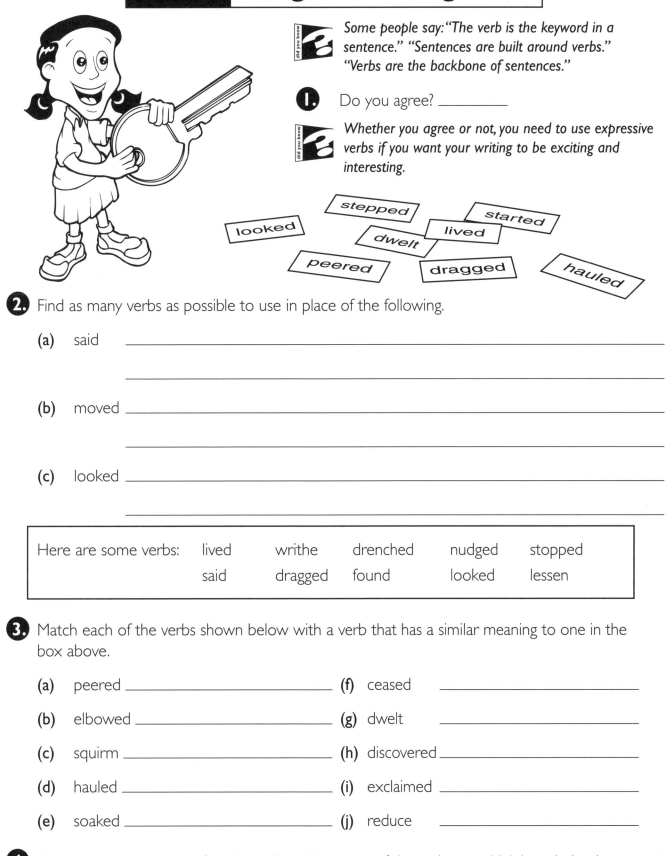

Some people say: "The verb is the keyword in a sentence." "Sentences are built around verbs." "Verbs are the backbone of sentences."

1. Do you agree? _____

Whether you agree or not, you need to use expressive verbs if you want your writing to be exciting and interesting.

stepped started looked lived dwelt peered dragged hauled

2. Find as many verbs as possible to use in place of the following.

(a) said _____

_____

(b) moved _____

_____

(c) looked _____

_____

Here are some verbs:	lived	writhe	drenched	nudged	stopped
	said	dragged	found	looked	lessen

3. Match each of the verbs shown below with a verb that has a similar meaning to one in the box above.

(a) peered _____

(b) elbowed _____

(c) squirm _____

(d) hauled _____

(e) soaked _____

(f) ceased _____

(g) dwelt _____

(h) discovered _____

(i) exclaimed _____

(j) reduce _____

4. Examine a book by your favorite author. List some of the verbs you think have helped to make the book more exciting and/or interesting.

The situation component tells us the circumstances in which the action takes place, such as:
- **when** something happens (It happened yesterday evening.)
- **where** something happens (It happened at the park.)
- **how** something happens (It happened like lightning.)
- **why** something happens (It happened because I was careless.)
- **how frequently** or the degree to which the action occurred (It happened very fast.)

1. Look at the following jokes. The situation components are in bold print.

2. What do the situation components in these jokes tell us? _____

3. Look at the answers to the jokes below. Underline the situation component. Write whether the part tells us **when**, **how**, **why**, **where** or **how** frequently.

(a) Why does a stork stand on one foot? He stands on one foot because he would fall

over if he lifted the other one. _____

(b) When were the dark ages?

The dark ages took place in the days of knights. _____

(c) Where does a worm go when he enters the cornfield?

He goes in one ear and out the other. _____

(d) Where are you if you're always behind the times?

You are standing at the back of the clock store. _____

(e) How would you get out of a locked music room?

I would play the piano very loudly until I found the right key. _____

Situation components: adverbial phrases

 Sometimes an adverb (a word that tells how, why, when or where about a verb) can be replaced by a group of words which has a similar meaning. This group of words is called an adverbial phrase.

I ran home quickly.

I ran home as fast as my legs could carry me.

1. Do you think it is better to use an adverb or an adverbial phrase?

_____ Why? _____

_____

2. Complete the sentence beginnings in column A with suitable phrases from column B by joining with a line.

In column C, indicate whether the adverbial phrases are:

M: *phrases of manner that show how something happens*
P: *phrases of place that show where something happens*
T: *phrases of time that show when something happens*
F: *phrases of frequency that show how often something happens*
D: *phrases of degree that make meaning stronger or weaker.*

Column A	Column B	Column C
The children ran across the park	in a cottage in the woods.	
Pete studies very hard	expertly through the surf.	
The mountaineer climbed carefully	when mother called.	
The apple pie was	very, very hot.	
The girl swam	at the new concert hall.	
The old man and woman lived	every night.	
The soprano sang sweetly	down the steep incline.	

3. On another piece of paper, write five sentences of your own. Include a different type of adverbial phrase in each.

Making sense of verb tenses

Did you know that **tense** means **time**?

It comes from the Latin word *tempus*. Tempus means time in Latin.

Verbs tell us what takes place in an action sequence.

But did you know that they also tell us the time of the action?

The time of the action is called the tense of the verb.
There are three main tenses: present tense, past tense and future tense.

1. Look at the pictures and captions below. Identify the tense of each verb.
Is it **present tense**, **past tense** or **future tense**?

(a)

| he ate his breakfast | he eats his breakfast | he will eat his breakfast |

_____   _____   _____

(b)

| he plays football | he will play football | he played football |

_____   _____   _____

2. Change the tenses of these verbs.

	present	past	future
(a)			She will run fast.
(b)		He read a book.	
(c)	She rides her bike.		

Reports are almost always written in the present tense because they refer to facts that exist now. Reports systematically organize and record factual information. They classify and describe a group of things that are alike.

1. Read the following report and underline the present tense verbs.

The Companions

The Companions are dog-walking machines that are particularly useful for people who live in apartments. They come in four different models. Model A is for small dogs like chihuahuas, terriers and miniature poodles. Model B is designed for medium-sized dogs such as spaniels and retrievers, while Model C is for large dogs like boxers, German shepherds and collies. Finally there is the deluxe model, which is designed for an owner and his or her dog to exercise together. Most dog owners have difficulty exercising their dogs so here is the answer to their problems.

Each Companion comes in five sections: a television screen, an electric treadmill, a timing device, speed adjustment and a harness.

The main unit of all the models has a television screen that shows park scenes and road scenes. This is to give dogs the feeling they are actually exercising outdoors, so they will not get bored while they are walking on the treadmill. The treadmill can be adjusted to suit any walking speed, so that owners of older dogs can make the machine go more slowly. The size of the treadmill varies according to the size of the dog for which it is designed. Attached to the front of the machine is a timer to allow the dog owner to decide how long the dog's walk will take. If the owner forgets about the dog, the machine switches off automatically when the time is up. There is also a harness to ensure that the dog cannot run away or leave the treadmill until the timer stops.

The Companion is a great way for busy people who don't have time to walk their dog, or for those who live far from a park. The machine is also popular with park rangers because they don't have to clean up after dogs. You should buy one today if you are a dog owner who lives in an apartment.

---

2. Reports are usually written about countries, special activities, machines, books or animals. What kind of report is this one?

_____

_____

3. The sections of a report are organized in a special way. Read the list of parts below and put them into the correct order.

- Summary comment/Use   _____

- Description   _____

- Dynamics (what each part does)   _____

- Classification/General statement   _____

- Title   _____

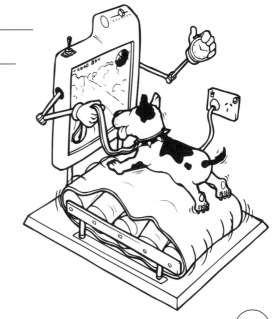

Verb tenses: the present tense

1. What does the **present tense** tell you about time? _____

_____

The present tense tells us about actions that happen again and again. It is used to tell us about habits.
"She rides her bike to school, but her brother walks."
"I collect stamps, but my friend collects coins."
"Mom cooks a roast dinner every Sunday."
It also tells us about facts that stay the same over a long period of time.
"I live in Boston and my pen pal lives in New York."
"My Dad works in a bank and my Mom teaches English in a high school."
"I like reading books written by Paul Jennings."
We also use the present tense when we say something that is always true about a person or about the world.
"Perth is the capital city of Western Australia."
"Water boils at 100 degrees centigrade."
"My friend comes from Korea."

2. In the space below, list 10 facts about an animal. Be sure to use the present (simple) tense. Include description, location, dynamics (habits) and classification in your list of facts.

(a) _____

(b) _____

(c) _____

(d) _____

(e) _____

(f) _____

(g) _____

(h) _____

(i) _____

(j) _____

3. Write an animal report using these 10 facts.

You have just learned about the present (simple) tense. Later on, you will learn about some other forms of present tense.

Writing present (simple) sentences

1. Can you list three reasons why you would use the present tense?

(a) _____

(b) _____

(c) _____

2. Write some present tense sentences of your own. In the first four sentences, tell us about habits of the following people.

(a) I _____

(b) My friend _____

(c) My mother _____

(d) My teacher _____

I have been to a swimming lesson.

3. Now write three sentences that tell about something that stays the same for a long time.

(a) _____

(b) _____

(c) _____

4. Write present tense sentences that express something that is always true about the following. The first one has been done for you.

(a) mammals — *A mammal is a warm-blooded animal that feeds its young on milk.*

(b) deserts — _____

(c) magnets — _____

(d) summer — _____

(e) your friend — _____

*Adverbs are words that tell **how**, **when** and **where** an action is done. Adverbs can also tell us how often something happens, that is, the **frequency** or **degree** to which the action has been performed. For example, "He **never** cleans his bedroom."*

1. The present (simple) tense is often found with adverbs of frequency.
Complete these sentences in the present (simple) tense.

(a) The friendly girl always _____ .

(b) My father usually _____ .

(c) The lazy dog often _____ .

(d) Sometimes I _____ .

2. Look at the adverbs in the following sentences. Complete the table below.
Decide whether they tell where, when, how (manner) or how much (degree/frequency).

(a) When a volcano erupts there is lava **everywhere**. It **often** buries whole villages as it rushes **wildly** down the mountain slopes.

(b) She tries to pat the puppy **gently** because he is so small, but **sometimes** she forgets and the puppy yaps **loudly** to warn her.

(c) The lion in the cage **near** the tiger roars **angrily** when he is hungry. He is fed **regularly** at six o'clock, but **occasionally** the keeper is late.

(d) She will come home **soon**. She is **seldom** late for the movies because she lives **close to** the theater.

(e) The scratch on the car **barely** shows. I can **easily** fix that.

(f) I **always** get up for school **later** than I should and then I have to rush **madly** around to get **there before** the class starts.

adverb	where	when	how	how much	adverb	where	when	how	how much
everywhere					soon				
often					seldom				
wildly					close to				
gently					barely				
sometimes					easily				
loudly					always				
near					later				
angrily					madly				
regularly					there				
occasionally					before				

What does the past tense tell us about time? The past tense tells us about actions that happened at a specific time in the past — actions that are now finished.

1. Draw pictures in the boxes below.

2. Write a sentence that tells what you did.
Write it on the line under the box.

Your sentences should all be written in the past (simple) tense because they refer to actions that are now finished. Past tense (just like present tense) also has other forms that you will learn about later.

(a) Something you did last night.

(c) Something you did last week.

(b) Something you did when you were a baby.

(d) Something you did three hours ago.

 Narratives (stories) are often written in past tense.

1. Explain why you think authors use past tense.

_____

_____

2. The excerpt below was taken from a narrative written by a student your age. The type of narrative is a **fable**.

Read the excerpt and underline all of the verbs you can find.

In the days when all the earth was flat, there lived in the village of Paetha, a wondrous potter named Pinon. Pinon was the greatest craftsperson in all of Greece and his work was admired throughout the land. Denos, Prince of Thessaly, had tried many times to persuade the potter to travel to his kingdom to become the Royal Potter. Prince Denos wanted to be the only person in the land to own the work of Pinon.

Each time a messenger was sent by the Prince, Pinon refused to be persuaded. The gold and jewels weighing down the messenger's saddlebags were returned to the Prince. The Prince became angrier and angrier at the potter's refusal to obey the royal request.

"Am I not the greatest Prince of all Greece?" he shouted at his advisers.

"How dare this worker of clay deny my wishes! You are my advisers. Find out what it is that he most desires in the world."

---

3. List all the verbs you found. Check whether they are in past or present tense.

verbs	past	present	verbs	past	present

4. Did you find any present tense verbs? _____ Suggest why the author changed from past to present tense.

_____

Past tense in narratives — 2

 Narratives (stories) are mostly told in past tense, but sometimes authors use the present tense for effect.

Here is the start of a short story. It is written in the present tense.

Janet is feeling sick. She coughs painfully, trying hard to cover her mouth as she does so, but with each cough, she feels weaker. She wants to lift her head from the pillow, but it feels heavy and leaden. Her head turns slowly to peer through the window next to her bed. Her eyes fix on the watery patterns forming on the glass and she is unsure whether the patterns really exist, or whether they are caused by the unwelcome tears that constantly seem to form in her eyes. Across the road she can see the distorted shapes of her friends playing happily in the puddles, splashing water and mud at each other and squealing with delight. "It's not fair," she is thinking. "I want to go out there and play too. Why did I have to catch the flu?"

 The present tense helps the readers feel as though they are right alongside the main character in the story.

Rewrite the passage above by changing it into the past tense.

Janet was feeling sick. _____

_____

_____

_____

_____

_____

_____

_____

_____

_____

_____

Verb tenses: talking about the future — 1

1. The children in the picture below are going to build a tree house during school vacation. Look at the objects they will be using.

2. The tree house is not built yet, so what tense will the children use to talk about it?

_____

3. Pretend you are one of the children and write what you will do with each of the objects. For example, you might write: **We will be using the rope to make a pulley, so we'll be able to get the timber into the tree.**

Verb tenses: talking about the future — 2

1. What do you think you will be doing ten years from now?

(a) Marital status _____

(b) Occupation _____

(c) Hobbies _____

(d) Transportation _____

2. Here is some information about some students at another school. Read the information about them and then write a sentence on the line below about what the students might like to do in the future. Begin your sentences with **"I think (insert name) is going to …"**

(a) Rebecca is very creative. She loves drawing comic characters.

_____

(b) Katherine likes children and they really like her too.

_____

(c) Dimitri enjoys riding his uncle's horse.

_____

(d) Jane enjoys using her Dad's tools to build her sister a playhouse.

_____

(e) Christine is the best in her class at math.

_____

(f) Jason's friends like eating at his house because he's a great cook.

_____

(g) Robert is very smart. Everyone chooses him on their quiz team.

_____

(h) Tam has been to the Europe. He had a great time.

_____

_____

(i) Jessie does a lot of voluntary work at the hospital.

_____

_____

*What did Jane say? She said, "My dog really likes salespeople." When we write exactly what Jane said, it is called **direct speech**. As you know, quotation marks are used to show which words are actually spoken.*

*When we report what Jane said to someone else, it is called **reported speech**. We do not need to use quotation marks with reported speech. In the example above, John is reporting to his Mom what Jane said to the salespeople.*

Look at the two statements again. Did you notice that the verb tense is the same for both statements? The direct statement and the reported statement are both written in the present tense. It is not always this easy. Sometimes the tense has to change.

*But how do we know if the tense should change? Fortunately for us, there are some simple rules. This is one of the rules: **if the action is still happening at the time it is reported, the tense stays the same.***

For example, Jane's dog still likes salespeople at the time her statement was reported by John. Fortunately Jane did not say that her dog likes to eat salespeople!

1. Change the following direct speech into reported statements.

(a) "I'm really, really tired," said David.

_____

(b) "I know you can do it," said Dad.

_____

(c) "It's not polite to push in the line," said the teacher.

_____

(d) "I'm going to the beach," said Rick.

_____

(e) "I have a new computer game," said Jackie.

_____

2. (a) Did the verb tense change? _____

(b) Did any other part of speech change? _____

If so, what changed? _____

There are instances where the tense stays the same for direct and reported speech.	You learned that the tense stays the same if the action is still occurring.	It also stays the same when the statement is about something that is accepted as a general truth.

Don't worry. Lightning never strikes twice in the same place.

You said lightning never strikes twice in the same place!

1. Change the following direct statements to reported speech.
Remember to use a new line for each new speaker.

(a) "This movie is very boring.
I don't think you'd like it," said Dylan.
"I still want to see it. Everyone in my class has
seen it," said Nicola.

_____

_____

_____

_____

(b) "Snakes are reptiles because they are cold-blooded," said Jenny
"Is that why they are slow moving in the winter?" asked Nancy.

_____

_____

_____

_____

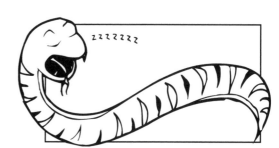

_____

1. Change the following to reported speech.

(a) "I'm really hungry. I want to go to the coffee shop and buy a donut."

_____

_____

_____

_____

(b) "I'm hungry too, but I don't like donuts."

_____

_____

_____

_____

(c) Christopher Columbus is trying to convince the Queen of Spain to finance his exploration. The Chief Adviser to the Queen objects.

_____

_____

_____

_____

_____

_____

When writers use direct and reported speech, the word "said" is often overused.

2. Find six words which can be used instead of "said."
Give examples of when you would use these words.

_____

_____

_____

_____

_____

Direct and reported speech — 4

You have learned so far that the tense does not change when direct speech becomes reported speech if (a) an action is still happening and (b) if the statement is a general truth. There is one more situation when the tense does not change. See if you can discover what it is.

1. Read this short play. Underline sentences that have reported speech in them.

Tom:	Jack tricked Miss Brown in science today.
Mom:	How did he do that? Miss Brown is very smart.
Tom:	We were talking about the different ways that animals move, and he said, "I know an animal that has 50 legs, but it can't walk at all."
Mom:	I've never heard of an animal like that. What did Miss Brown say?
Tom:	She said to Jack, "You should tell the class about it."
Mom:	I'd like to hear about such a strange creature too.
Tom:	Well, Jack stood up and said, "The creature I'm thinking of is a centipede that's been cut in half."
Mom:	What did Miss Brown say?
Tom:	She just laughed with the class and then we went on with the lesson.

Notice the examples above show Tom reporting the direct speech of Jack and Miss Brown to his mother.

2. Look at the sentences you have underlined.

(a) The first part of each sentence is written in which tense? _____

(b) The reported speech is written in which tense? _____

3. Rewrite the sentences you have underlined by making the whole sentence into reported speech. You will not need to change the tenses but you will need to change the pronouns.

_____

_____

_____

4. Write the third rule that tells when tense does not change.

_____

_____

_____

5. Think of some jokes. On another piece of paper, write a short play like the one above. Use your own joke in it.

Now that you know the three rules about keeping the tense the same when you change direct speech into reported speech, you need to understand when it becomes necessary to change the tense.

1. Read this short newspaper article.

Burglar Quacks Up!

An unlucky intruder bit off more than he could chew when he tried to break into a suburban home yesterday. His attempts at climbing in through the bathroom window alerted Harvey, the family duck, who raced to the rescue. Harvey's sudden appearance upset the burglar so much he fell head first through the window, hitting his head on the bath and knocking himself unconscious. Neighbors said they heard Harvey's quacking and contacted the home owners, Mr. and Mrs. Henderson, who were surprised to find the would-be thief still out cold on the floor, with a very proud Harvey standing guard. "We weren't sure about having a duck for a guard dog," Mr. Henderson said. "But after this incident, we wouldn't swap Harvey for the world. He's a real hero."

(a) Underline the reported speech in blue.
(b) Underline the direct speech in red.

2. Change the reported speech you have underlined in blue into direct speech.

_____

_____

_____

_____

_____

_____

3. Change the direct speech you have underlined in red into indirect speech.

_____

_____

_____

_____

_____

_____

4. What did you notice about the tenses you used?

_____

_____

5. Change the following into direct speech.
(a) He explained that he never ate seafood. _____

_____

(b) He said he was waiting for the bus. _____

_____

The marks used to show the words that are actually spoken in direct speech are called quotation marks. There are definite rules to show you how to use quotation marks correctly.

1. Read the story and underline the words that are spoken.

It was close to dinner time and the family had only eaten a small lunch. Grandma Barnes looked up from her knitting and sighed. "I'm really hungry," she remarked. "I wonder what your mother is cooking for dinner tonight."

"It's a secret," declared Katie, who was only five years old. "Mom's cooking tuna pie because she knows it's your favorite."

"If it's a secret," whispered twelve-year-old Amy, "then you shouldn't have told Grandma. Now it's not a secret anymore".

"Yes, it is," protested Katie. "Grandma can keep a secret."

"Maybe so, Katie, but who is she keeping the secret from?" retorted Amy.

Mrs. Barnes entered the family room. "Well, we *were* going to have tuna pie for dinner," she said, "but unfortunately your father bought four cans of *cat food* tuna instead of …"

Mr. Barnes interrupted. "Well, you didn't say what kind of tuna you wanted."

"But, Dad," stated Amy, "we don't even own a cat!" She shook her head in astonishment at her father's strange logic. "Now, what can we have?"

"I know," suggested Katie, "let's have stuffed bikini and salami instead".

"I think you mean stuffed zucchini, Katie," answered Mrs. Barnes. "I could probably manage that. There's a recipe for it in my 'How to Cook Italian Dishes' book, but I think the salami's off the menu. It'll be too hot for you, dear."

"No, it won't be. I can blow on it," protested Katie.

Amy shook her head as if to signal that she wasn't really a member of such an illogical family. "Mom, will you explain it to her!"

Mrs. Barnes looked at the hungry faces of her family and smiled. "I have the perfect solution. Who is responsible for this situation?"

"Dad!" the children shouted.

"Then who should solve the problem?"

"Dad!" they repeated.

"Okay, dear. I guess you'll have to get the car out of the garage and drive to the fish store," smiled Mrs. Barnes.

"I've got a better idea. Why don't I just 'let my fingers do the walking' by picking up the phone and ordering home-delivered pizza instead."

"Oh, no! 'Super-Dad' to the rescue," groaned Amy.

Sometimes the words that are actually said come first. Sometimes they come last, and sometimes they are split by an explanation of who is speaking.

2. Quotation marks have also been used for two other purposes. What are they?

(a) _____

(b) _____

3. On another piece of paper, list the words that have been used instead of "said."

Making sense of conditionals

"If" may be a little word, but it is a very strong word.
It can act as a link to show how one action is the cause of another.
It can link two clauses together and show how they relate to each other.
"If" shows the condition that causes the second action, so we call
clauses that have "if" in them conditional clauses.
There are four kinds of conditions:

- *the general condition;*
- *the first condition;*
- *the second condition; and*
- *the third condition.*

*When the condition refers to facts, it is called the **general condition**.*

It stops if you push the button. (function) 	*If it has a square base, it is a square pyramid. (fact)* 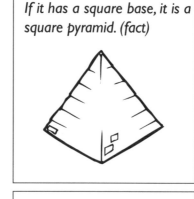	*If you pull this lever, the door will open. (causes)* 
If you pour oil on water, it will float. (scientific fact) 	*If his mother calls, he always comes home immediately. (behavior)* 	*If he comes now, tell him I'm not home. (instructions)* 

1. Is the tense used in the "if" clauses above ☐ present ☐ past or ☐ future?

2. Now write some general conditional statements of your own.

(a) scientific fact _____

(b) behavior _____

(c) causes _____

(d) function _____

(e) fact _____

(f) instructions _____

 World Teachers Press®

When the condition refers to predictions that seem likely to happen, it is called the first condition.

(a) If it rains, we'll get wet.

(c) If they're late, they'll miss the start of the game.

(e) If you come with me, I'll pay your fare.

(b) If you stand in this line, you'll get served quickly.

(d) If you give her your program, she'll get you an autograph.

(f) If they don't come soon, he'll have to go in.

1. Which tense do the "if" clauses use? _____

2. Which tense does the second clause use? _____

The second clauses have helpers in front of the verb. List the pronouns and helpers used in the second clauses.

(a) *we will*_____ (c) _____ (e) _____

(b) _____ (d) _____ (f) _____

3. Write some first conditional sentences of your own.

(a) _____

_____

(b) _____

_____

(c) _____

_____

Conditionals: the second condition

When the condition refers to predictions that are unlikely to happen, or could not happen, it is called the second condition.

The "if clauses" use past tense verbs.
The verbs in the other clause have helper words.

1. Write the "if clauses" from above and underline the verbs.

(a) _____

(b) _____

(c) _____

(d) _____

The same rule applies when you use the word "wish," because wish suggests that the situation is unreal, or unlikely to happen.

2. Read the wishes below and add some of your own.

3. Discuss the use of **bought** and **brought** with your teacher.

When the condition refers to the past, where the prediction did not occur, it is called the third condition.

> If I hadn't been talking on the phone, I would have noticed what he was doing.

> If I hadn't seen him, he would have chewed Dad's socks as well.

> If you had valued those socks, you would have put them in the closet.

1. Add some comments of your own on another piece of paper using the third conditional.

2. Did you notice the verbs in the "if clauses" needed a helper? Underline the helper in each "if clause."

3. Did the second clause also need a helper?   Yes ☐   No ☐

4. Was the present tense used at all?   Yes ☐   No ☐

5. Below, write some of the ways in which the following situations could have been avoided.

(a)   (b)   (c)

(a) _____

_____

(b) _____

_____

(c) _____

_____

Using conditionals in expositions

An exposition is a special class of writing in which the writer expresses his or her point of view. People often write expositions if they wish to argue a point or persuade readers to consider their point of view. They may use conditionals to do this.

1. Read this short exposition about recycling.
Identify the conditionals and underline them.

The Importance of Recycling

As the population grows, so does the amount of garbage that people are producing. This is made worse by the fact that many new materials produced today do not rot and break down quickly like the natural materials that were used in the past. If garbage doesn't break down quickly, it accumulates. Local councils report that they have a huge problem trying to find new ways to dispose of garbage such as plastics, rubber tires, aluminum cans and polystyrene containers. If we can't dispose of them, we need to find a way to reuse these materials through recycling. Scientists will have to solve the problem very soon or the population could be faced with diseases and pollution that affect health and the environment. For this reason we need to become very serious about recycling everything that we possibly can. If I were a politician, I would make it a law that everyone has to recycle their garbage.

Consider what could happen if we don't begin seriously recycling our garbage. Tons and tons of garbage would have to be burned. This would cause more carbon dioxide to leak into the atmosphere and global warming would increase. If global warming increases, the sea level will rise and many low-lying countries will disappear. Scientists warn us that we must stop releasing carbon dioxide into the air, because if we don't, vegetation will be affected and so will the animal life on Earth. Furthermore, garbage provides an ideal breeding ground for disease-carrying animals like rats, mice, cockroaches and mosquitoes. Hospitals would not be able to cope if plagues occurred and without clean water, humans could not survive.

So you can see why I think it is important to begin recycling right now. If people had started recycling their garbage 10 years ago, we would not be facing such enormous problems today. However, if we all work together now, we can solve this problem.

GLASS

2. (a) Give an example of the general condition.

_____

(b) Give an example of the first condition.

_____

(c) Give an example of the second condition.

_____

(d) Give an example of the third condition.

_____

Describing characters: using adjectives

1. What is an adjective? _____

2. Why do authors and poets use them? _____

_____

3. Read the description below. It was written by Scott, who likes to read and is very good with words. This is his description of Count Dracula. Scott uses a lot of describing words to paint a picture of Dracula.

Dracula

I was walking down a foggy London street to get away from my hotel room. My business had been going well in London, but at night I had nothing to do, so I was in the habit of going for a walk. It was about midnight and even though it was a full moon, it was quite dark. Suddenly, I felt a fluttering on the back of my neck. I turned around and saw a tiny bat flapping in front of my eyes. It wasn't pleasant, but something even more unpleasant was to come. It was then that I saw him — Dracula.

He walked towards me, tall and straight. He looked like a count, but his appearance was evil. His eyes stared cruelly at me from under black, bushy eyebrows that joined in the middle to make a straight line. His eyes gleamed red, making him look sly and untrustworthy. He was dressed like a count, too, in black and white clothing, almost concealed by a dark, billowing cape that dragged behind him. But it was his face that looked the scariest and made my blood chill. His pale, white skin showed that he needed more blood and his thin build revealed that his diet was not normal. His long, dank, black hair was dirty and needed washing. It hung down, but didn't hide his ears that looked too big for his head. They came to a point at the top — a bit like a pixie — but he was no fairytale. He was real and so were the sharp white fangs that jutted from his mouth. That mouth was ugly. It pulled back into a permanent snarl, never smiling from below a stubby nose that was too short for his face.
I started to run, but I was no match for him. He pounced on me and I felt the piercing fangs sink into my neck.

4. List the adjectives that Scott used to describe Dracula.

_____ _____ _____

_____ _____

_____ _____

_____ _____

_____ _____

Description: tenses

1. Read Scott's description of Dracula again. Would you find a description of this kind in fictional or factual writing? _____

Is the description mostly written in ☐ present tense, ☐ past tense or ☐ future tense?

2. Now read the following description about fish. It is part of an animal report written by a student named Robert.

Fish are cold-blooded, gill-breathing vertebrates. There are more than 25,000 species of fish living in oceans throughout the world and they vary a lot in appearance. Some are brightly colored and graceful, such as the angelfish, while others, such as the piranha, are gray and ugly. The shape of most fish is long and tapering to help them move swiftly and they have smooth, streamlined bodies to help them move efficiently. Four kinds of spiny fins are used to propel them in the water. Their top fins help them to remain upright, while their side fins assist them to swim up, down and forward, as well as to stop. Their bottom fins help them to stay the right way up and their tail fins, which are vertical, help them to turn.

3. This is not all of Robert's description, but it is enough to enable you to examine the tense he has used and compare it with the tense used by Scott in his description of Dracula. Compare the descriptions and write what you noticed about the tenses used.

_____

_____

4. Now compare the adjectives. Can you see a difference in the kind of descriptive words used by the two writers? _____

_____

5. Robert has used the words "brightly," "efficiently," and "swiftly" in his description. Are these adjectives? _____ If not, what part of speech are they? _____

6. Do you think it is necessary to write an adjective for every noun? _____

7. Read the following sentences.
   (a) The sleek, black, shiny, stealthy panther kept low to the ground as it stalked the shy, small, dappled, fawn grazing by its mother.
   (b) The star shone brightly on top of the colorful, decorated, fancy, green Christmas tree.

8. What would you do to improve them? Rewrite them on another piece of paper.

Description: metaphor

*In Scott's description, you were able to find many adjectives. Using adjectives is not the only way writers paint word pictures. Writers also use metaphor. A metaphor is a way of comparing one thing with another by saying it **is** that thing.*
For example, "The city is a fairyland of lights at holiday time."

1. Read the following poem.

My Lucky Escape

The sea was a shimmering blanket
the sun was a lamp on high
the sky was a clear blue ceiling
the wind sang a lullaby.
As I floated on my surfboard
as I bobbed like a cork in the sea
and I wished we could float here forever
just the seagulls, the dolphins and me.
Then I heard a soft voice like a mermaid
like a mermaid calling to me
I opened my eyes for an instant
and what do you think I could see?
A wave building up on the skyline
like a mountain growing at sea
my heart skipped a beat for a moment
in an instant I turned to flee.

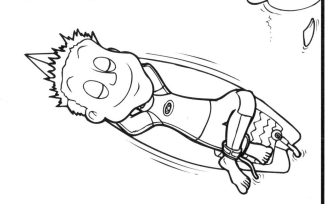

I paddled as fast as a steam train
my arms were paddles of steel
and I landed safe on the warm, white sand
where I lay, for a while, like a seal.
I still go down to the ocean
I still use my board in the sea
but I'm careful to stay awake and alert —
a watery grave's not for me.

2. What metaphor is used for these?

(a) the sea _____

(b) the sky _____

(c) the sun _____

(d) the surfer's arms _____

3. Invent some metaphors of your own to describe the words below.

(a) winter _____

(b) a willow tree _____

(c) a ballerina _____

(d) cheese _____

(e) the ocean _____

(f) a steam engine _____

(g) your best friend _____

Description: similes

 *Authors and poets use similes to help them paint word pictures. Although similes are another way to compare two things, they are different from metaphors. When you use a metaphor, you say that one thing **is** something else. When you use a simile, you say it is **like** something else.*

1. Here are some similes. In what way are they different from metaphors?

(a) The moon is like a golden smile.

(b) She is like a ray of sunshine.

(c) His clothes hung on him like a scarecrow.

_____

_____

_____

2. Read the poem "My Lucky Escape" again. Write how the poet describes the following.

(a) The way the surfer bobbed in the sea. _____

(b) The soft voice. _____

(c) The wave building up. _____

(d) The way the surfer paddled. _____

(e) The way the surfer lay on the sand. _____

3. Now write some similes of your own to describe the things listed.

(a) thunder _____

(e) garlic _____

(b) football _____

(f) twilight _____

(c) gorilla _____

(g) diamonds _____

(d) lips _____

(h) puppy _____

Making sense of words: idioms — 1

1. What is an idiom? _____

_____

2. The cartoons below about the theater may help you understand what idioms are and why we use them. Match the cartoons to the idioms and explain what each one means.

(a) He always has to be **in the limelight.**

_____

_____

_____

(b) He's not a good actor. In fact I think he's **quite a ham.**

_____

_____

_____

(c) You'd have to be as **mad as a hatter** to be a stage director.

_____

_____

_____

(d) I don't really like acting, but it **brings home the bacon.**

_____

_____

_____

(e) He is always **full of beans.**

_____

_____

_____

3. Why do we use idioms?

1. Look at the idioms on the previous page.

2. Which one is a bit different from the others? _____

How is it different? _____

_____

3. Here are three more that are like it. Draw your cartoons.

(a)   She is as gentle as a lamb and her sister is as quiet as a mouse.

(b)   I think I'll do my homework
because it's raining cats and dogs.

(c)   This homework is a breeze.
I'll sail through it easily.

4. Explain what these idioms mean.

(a)   She is as cold as a fish. _____

(b)   The vase you bought is a white elephant. _____

(c)   The night was as black as pitch. _____

(d)   It is twenty kilometers as the crow flies. _____

(e)   I wish you would pull yourself together. _____

Grammar: newspaper articles

 There are many different kinds of writing that you need to know to become a really successful writer.

1. List some of the types you have learned. _____

_____

 Each genre has something special about its structure that makes it different from the others. However, it is not only the structure of genres that you need to know about — each genre also has other special features.

2. Here is a list of features that may be different for different genres.
Match the feature with its meaning.

(a)	verb tense	• not based on thoughts and feelings
(b)	point of view	• words that can connect one sentence or idea to another
(c)	vocabulary	• shows when an action has taken place
(d)	paragraphing	• a collection of words
(e)	indirect/direct speech	• indicates whether the words were those of the speaker or of a witness
(f)	linking words	• a grouping of sentences which develop one particular point
(g)	objectivity	• refers to the person who is speaking, is being spoken about, or is being spoken to

A newspaper article is a special form of writing. It has grammatical features as well as a special structure.

3. Here are parts that make up the structure of a newspaper article. Write the structural feature next to its correct explanation.

next most important points

| lead | | byline | headline | conclusion |

(a) _____   • the title of an article

(b) _____   • the writer's name and where the news originated

(c) _____   • introduction that may tell who, what, where, when, why and how

(d) _____   • supporting details and facts

_____

(e) _____   • some of the consequences and future leads

A newspaper article can differ from other forms of writing in the point of view from which it is written.

1. Read the newspaper article below.

Knave of Hearts Shuffled off to Prison

Card Kingdom

By Wee Willie Winky

There was cause for celebration in the Kingdom of Hearts, with the arrest yesterday of the man who allegedly stole the Queen's favorite tarts. The Queen, who was said to be very upset over the disappearance of the Royal tarts, reported that she was delighted with the arrest. "The impertinence of that knave. He was given the freedom of the palace and this is how he repaid our hospitality," she said. "I don't know what to think of Card Kingdom these days. Last week Tom, the Piper's son, ran off with the royal bacon and the week before that, little Jack Horner demolished the Christmas Pie. We have to stop this kind of vandalism in the kingdom or the tourism industry will suffer." The palace guards, however, received special recognition from the Queen for their heroism. The captain of the Royal Guards was very modest when interviewed. "I must thank the public for their cooperation," he said. "Once we released a description of the thief and the direction of his escape, it was the action of the citizens that helped us to locate him." When asked what would happen to the knave now, the Captain replied that the severity of the punishment would have to fit the crime. The knave will be on a bread and water diet for a very long time.

*Did you notice that the journalist's own ideas and feelings are not included? This is because journalists are reporting facts. When you report facts you use pronouns like he, she, they, it, them, their, his, her, or which. You can also use people's names. This is called the **third person point of view**.*

2. Underline the pronouns in the article.

3. Which pronouns are not third person pronouns? _____

_____

*Notice how the pronouns change when direct speech is used. To give your own point of view use I, me, us and we. This is called the **first person point of view**. For example, if you write "I think ..." you are writing from the first person point of view.*

4. Write three sentences in the **first person** point of view.

(a) _____

(b) _____

(c) _____

The second person point of view is when the pronoun "you" is used. For example, if you write "You probably think ..." you are writing from the second person point of view.

5. Write three sentences in the **second person** point of view.

(a) _____

(b) _____

(c) _____

World Teachers Press®

1. Read the statements below. ✔ the statements you expect to see in a newspaper report. **(a)** ☐ **(b)** ☐ **(c)** ☐ **(d)** ☐ **(e)** ☐ **(f)** ☐

*Remember, newspaper reports should only present facts. They are written from the **third person** point of view.*

2. Put a ✔ next to statements written from the **third person** point of view.

(a) ☐ Mr. Brown said the road was still dangerous in spite of changes to the speed limit. He said the curve in the road had caused many accidents in the past and it would not be long before a death occurred.

(b) ☐ I thought that the accident could have been avoided if the man checked his equipment before climbing the ladder.

(c) ☐ Your report on the behavior of students made me very angry. I think you should stick to the facts when you publish reports.

(d) ☐ One of England's richest men today donated all of his wealth to charity. Mr. Robert Brown-Smith said he was tired of the stress of making money and that he wanted to go and live on a desert island where there were no phones to annoy him.

(e) ☐ You need to relax more. Go to the movies this weekend and enjoy a good film.

(f) ☐ The jury was not told the prisoner had faced the court on three previous occasions before the latest, successful prosecution was launched against him.

3. Underline the pronouns that helped you to make your decision about points of view.

4. Three of the sentences are not written from the third person point of view. Rewrite them in the **third person** point of view.

(a) _____

_____

(b) _____

_____

(c) _____

_____

Using active and passive voice

*Another special feature about newspaper articles is that they use the **passive voice** rather than the **active voice**. To understand the **active** and **passive voices**, you need to be able to recognize parts of a sentence, for example, the verb, the subject and the object in a sentence.*

Look at these pictures.

1. Complete these sentences below to explain the subject and the object of the sentence.

(a) Who broke the vase?
Steven broke the vase.

_____ is the subject in this sentence.

(b) What did Steven break?
Steven broke the vase.

The _____ is the object in this sentence.

(c) Who washed the car?
Dad washed the car.

_____ is the subject in this sentence.

(d) What did Dad wash?
Dad washed the car.

The _____ is the object in this sentence.

The "doer" of an action is the subject of the sentence. Therefore, Steven is the "doer" (subject) in the first sentence and Dad is the "doer" (subject) in sentence (c).
The "receiver" of the action is the object in the sentence. Therefore, the vase is the "receiver" (object) in sentence (b) and the car is the "receiver" (object) in sentence (d).
Most verbs express an action, so verbs are often called "doing words" or "action" words.

2. The "doing words" (verbs) in the two sentences are _____ and _____.

The sentences above are written in the active voice because the subject did the action (the verb) to the receiver.

3. Write two sentences in the **active voice**.

(i) _____

(ii) _____

 World Teachers Press®

More about active voice

1. Look at the following pictures and write sentences in the active voice to describe what is happening/has happened.

(a) _____

(b) _____

(c) _____

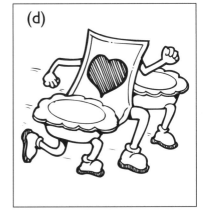  

(d) _____

(e) _____

(f) _____

2. Underline the subjects of your sentences in red.

3. Underline the verbs you have used in blue.

4. Underline the objects in your sentences in green.

5. Draw a picture of your own. Write a sentence in active voice to describe what has happened in your picture.

*The passive voice is used when we do not need, or want, to say who did the action. When we say what happens to people or things — what is done to them — we use the **passive voice**. It is used when we are describing what has happened to something. For example,*

> The window was broken last night.

If I do not know who did the action, I use the passive voice to say what was done to the window. The window (the receiver) was mentioned first.

If I am concentrating on the window, I mention it first and describe what happened to it.

> The window was broken by your little girl.

Your dog dug up my daffodils.

This is an active sentence.
The action is mentioned first.

My daffodil bed has been destroyed by your dog.

This is a passive sentence.
The receiver of the action is mentioned first.

1. Underline the passive sentences below.

(a) My bike is being repaired today.

(b) Her calculator was stolen from her desk.

(c) The cat scratched the baby.

(d) The car was hit by the 7:30 train.

(e) The boys laughed at her joke.

(f) The ice cream melted in the sun.

(g) The poem was written by John.

(h) They went to the zoo yesterday.

2. How are the verbs in the passive sentences alike? _____

_____

_____

3. Write a passive sentence to tell about something that was done to you. _____

_____

Making nouns from other parts of speech

 *The passive form of writing uses a lot of **nouns** that have been made from other **parts of speech**. Making a word into a noun is a "nominalization." You can nominalize a word (make it into a noun) by adding a suffix to it. A suffix is a syllable placed at the end of a word. It usually changes the word into a different part of speech. For example, if you add the suffix "–ance" to the word **perform**, you can make a new word **performance**. You have made the verb into a **noun**.*

1. Read the report on page 56 again. This time, identify the words that have been nominalized. Underline them in red.

 There are several noun suffixes in the newspaper report about the Knave of Hearts. Here are some of them: –ism, –dom, –ance, –tion, –ity and –ence.

2. Write the base word in the spaces provided and indicate the change that has taken place to the base word. The first one has been done for you.

(a) *celebrate — verb to a noun*   –tion

(b) _____   _____

(c) _____   _____

(d) _____   _____

(e) _____   _____

(f) _____   _____

(g) _____   _____

(h) _____   _____

(i) _____   _____

(j) _____   _____

(k) _____   _____

(l) _____   _____

3. Nominalize (make nouns from) these verbs.

(a) criticize _____   (f) correct _____

(b) adopt _____   (g) collect _____

(c) attract _____   (h) annoy _____

(d) resist _____   (i) reside _____

(e) equal _____   (j) bore _____

Newspaper headlines

Newspaper headlines are designed to catch the reader's attention. Sometimes they use words that have more than one meaning (for example, ambiguous words such as "Knave of Hearts Shuffled off to Prison) to attract your attention.

1. Underline any ambiguous words you can find in the headlines listed below.

The New York Times
18 September 1998

(a) ☐ Tornado Claims Seven Lives

(b) ☐ Eagles Fly Home Against the Hawks

(c) ☐ Dam Construction Delayed by Site

(d) ☐ School Burns Down

(e) ☐ Man Bites Dog

(f) ☐ Students Strike for Better Conditions

(g) ☐ Hockey Star Injured

(h) ☐ Victims Awarded Compensation

(i) ☐ Aussies Excel at Atlanta

(j) ☐ Record Smashed by Window

2. Headlines are almost always written in the simple or the simple present tense. Next to the headlines above, put a ✔ next to those that are written in past tense. Put a ✗ next to those that are written in present tense.

3. Look through a newspaper and see if you can find any headlines that use ambiguous words. Cut these out and make a collage on another piece of paper.

4. Select one of the headlines and write your own short newspaper article on a piece of paper.

5. The following headlines are ambiguous. They mean something different to what you may first guess. Write some of their possible meanings in the spaces provided.

(a) Fly Traps Spider _____

_____

_____

(b) Three Strikes — You're In _____

_____

_____

Exploring news articles

1. Read the passage below.

Giant Criticizes Security Measures

Story Book Land

By BB Wolf

The giant from Cloud Castle lodged a complaint today, charging Jack from Beanstalk Lane with vandalism and grand larceny. The wealthy giant, who is noted for his love of gold, lashed out at the palace guard for an apparent lack of security in the Kingdom. The giant's hen, which reputedly lays golden eggs, was stolen in the early hours of the morning while the giant was listening to a performance from his golden harp. The maid was dozing by the fire. When she woke up she saw Jack disappearing out of the door with a hen under his arm. "Not only did he steal my hen, but he also chopped down my beanstalk — my only means of transportation from Cloud Castle. This kind of vandalism tests the tolerance of a pacifist like me and it must be stopped. I want action and I intend to get it." The palace guard reacted to this stinging criticism by promising the population that security would be tightened in the future to avoid this kind of incident happening again. Bail was denied and Jack was taken to prison.

2. List any words that are unfamiliar to you. Check their meanings.

_____

_____

_____

3. Underline in red pen any passive sentences in the passage.

4. Can you find any words that have been nominalized?
Circle, in blue pen, any nominalizations you can find.

5. Examine the headline.

(a) Is it past or present tense? _____

(b) Does it catch the reader's attention? Why/Why not? _____

_____

(c) Write an alternative headline to the one given. _____

_____

(d) On a piece of paper, list ten verbs used in the article. Next to each verb, write its tense.

6. Underline any direct speech you can find in blue pen.

Verb tenses: using verb tenses

 You have learned there are three main **verb tenses**: *the present, the past and the future. You have also learned about the simple present, the simple past and the simple future tenses.*

1. (a) Tense means __ __ __ __.

(b) The tense of a verb tells us __ __ __ __ an action takes place.

(c) These three tenses are p __ __ __ , p__ __ __ __ __ __ and f __ __ __ __ __.

Each of these tenses have other forms. The most important are **simple**, **continuous** *and* **perfect**.
These forms tell us about the completeness of an action, that is, whether an action is still taking place, whether it has been completed, or whether it will be completed sometime in the future. They are displayed in the table below.

	present	past	future
simple	I wash	I washed	I will wash
continuous	I am washing	I was washing	I will be washing
perfect	I have washed	I had washed	I will have washed

2. Use the same pattern shown in the table using verbs of your choice.

	present	past	future
simple			
continuous			
perfect			
simple			
continuous			
perfect			
simple			
continuous			
perfect			
simple			
continuous			
perfect			

Verb tenses: making sense of perfect tense

 Perfect tense *shows an action has been completed.*

Meet the Perfect family.

Miss **Present Perfect**   Master **Past Perfect**   Miss **Future Perfect**

Write three things that each of the Perfect children might say about the following subjects.
The first one has been done for you.

Writing a letter

Miss Present Perfect: *"I write a letter to my pen pal every week."*
Master Past Perfect: *"I wrote to Grandma last week."*
Miss Future Perfect: *"I will write to Aunt Jane as soon as I finish watching this movie."*

(a) **Washing the dishes**
Miss Present Perfect: _____

Master Past Perfect: _____

Miss Future Perfect: _____

(b) **The environment**
Miss Present Perfect: _____

Master Past Perfect: _____

Miss Future Perfect: _____

(c) **The weather**
Miss Present Perfect: _____

Master Past Perfect: _____

Miss Future Perfect: _____

(d) **Vacation**
Miss Present Perfect: _____

Master Past Perfect: _____

Miss Future Perfect: _____

Verb tenses: the present continuous

 Continuous tenses are sometimes called "progressive" tenses. They refer to actions that are not completed.

Meet the Continuous family. They are Mrs. **Past Continuous**, Mr. **Future Continuous** and Miss **Present Continuous**.

First, meet Miss **Present Continuous**.

Miss **Present Continuous** likes to talk about things that are taking place right now. She also likes to talk about actions that are currently happening, even if she's not doing them at the moment she is speaking.

Miss **Present Continuous** also likes to talk about activities that she is planning for the future.

Write two things Miss Present Continuous might say about the following topics.

(a) Music _____

_____

(b) Travel _____

_____

(c) Hobbies _____

_____

(d) School _____

_____

Verb tenses: past continuous — I

Meet Mrs. **Past Continuous**.
Mrs. **Past Continuous** talks about actions that were in progress at some time in the past.

⟶

The band **continued playing** while the *Titanic* sank beneath the waves.

Sometimes Mrs. **Past Continuous** talks about two actions going on at the same time.

⟶

The girls **were doing** science projects, while the boys were using the computers.

Mrs. **Past Continuous** also likes to talk about her past habits.

⟶

When I was a young girl, we **were** always **playing** in the street.

1. Write what Mrs. **Past Continuous** might say about these pictures of her neighbors — Mr. and Mrs. Lee and their son James. What were the Lee's doing yesterday?

(a) Mrs. Lee _____

_____

(b) Mr. Lee _____

_____

(c) James Lee _____

_____

2. Complete these sentences using **past continuous** tense.

(a) She _____ _____ a cup of coffee when I walked into the kitchen.

(b) When he was a boy, he _____ always _____ for shells on the beach.

(c) The birds _____ _____ while the bees _____

_____ from flower to flower.

(d) I _____ _____ for you from 5:30 until 6:00. Where were you?

*Have you ever had a really vivid dream? Most people have them. Sometimes you can remember the dream when you wake up and you want to tell someone. Most likely you will use the **past continuous** tense to relate your dream to the listener. This is how Georgia told her Mom about her dream.*

I was swimming in the state championships and when the starting gun went off everyone dived in except me because my feet were stuck to the block. They eventually became unstuck but the rest of the swimmers had nearly finished.

Here are some pictures of dreams.
Use the past continuous tense to write about each dream in the space provided.

(a) _____
_____
_____
_____
_____
_____
_____

(b) _____
_____
_____
_____
_____
_____

(c) _____
_____
_____
_____
_____
_____

Finally, meet **Mr. Future Continuous**.
He likes to tell you what he intends to do in the future.
Look at these pictures and write what he is thinking of doing.

1. **(a)** This time tomorrow I will be

_____

_____

(b) This time next week I'll be

_____

_____

2. **Mrs. Future Continuous** has different plans for **Mr. Future Continuous** tomorrow.
Look at the pictures and write what she thinks he will be doing.

(a) This time tomorrow he will be

_____

_____

(b) This time next week he will be

_____

_____

3. Write a sentence about what you will be doing tomorrow using the future

continuous tense. _____

_____

Now use the **future continuous tense** to write about the following.

(a) Write about two things you will be doing tomorrow.

_____

_____

(b) Write about two things you would like to be doing during your next vacation.

_____

_____

(c) Write about something you would like to do in your future occupation.

_____

_____

(d) Write about two things you will probably be doing this weekend.

_____

_____

(e) What do you hope to be doing in ten years' time?

_____

_____

(f) In the year 2030, people may have a greater life span than they do now. What else might they be doing? _____

_____

_____

_____

Merrivale Elementary
384 Reid Road
Philadelphia, PA

Ms. Shell
Editor, *Community News*
24 Scarborough Road
Philadelphia, PA

Dear Editor,

I **am writing** to tell you about an activity the students of Merrivale Elementary School **have planned**. We **were learning** about people who help others when one of our students **suggested** our class could plan a way to **raise** money.

At first, we **planned** to raise money for a local charity. Last month, however, our students saw a documentary about children who **are living** in other countries. They **learned** there were many children who **had never attended** school because their parents **were** unable to afford an education for them. Our students **felt** so sorry for the children that they **wrote** to Aid Agency and **offered** to help.

Since then, they **have been fund-raising**. Each week the students **plan** a different activity for the whole school to enjoy. The other students in the school **are** happy to cooperate and everybody **has joined** in the project. By the time you **receive** this letter, Merrivale Elementary **will have raised** sufficient money to fund the education of a least ten children for a year. We **want** to help at least fifty children by the end of the year.

Within the next two weeks Merrivale students **will appear** on TV to present the money the school **has raised** to an agency representative. We hope this will inspire other schools to want to join our program in the future.

I **am asking** you, therefore, to help provide publicity by writing an article about the program, so more people **will be aware** of it.

Yours sincerely,

Mrs. Smith
Principal

1. Read the letter on the previous page and identify the tense of the verbs in bold print. Write them on the table provided.

Form of the verb	Examples
present simple	
present continuous	
present perfect	
past simple	
past continuous	
past perfect	
future simple	
future continuous	
future perfect	

2. Correct these sentences.

(a) The goalkeeper leaps forward and deflected the goal.

_____

(b) I was eating some bread when I bited into a piece of plastic.

_____

(c) She is listening to the stereo while her husband cooked dinner.

_____

(d) I had completed reading my book by the time the game starts.

_____

(e) I will go swimming when I finished doing my homework.

_____

(f) We have beat that team every time we played them.

_____

Auxiliaries: identifying "helper" verbs

*Did you notice in some of the tenses the verb needed a "**helper**" (**auxiliary**) verb? Helpers are words like: **am, is, are, was** and **were** (also called the verb "**to be**"). Other "helpers" are the verb "**to have**" which includes words such as: **have, has, had,** and the verb "**to do**" which includes words such as: **do, does** and **did**. Sometimes the verb is "helped" by words like: **shall, will, would, may, might, can** and **could**. Auxiliary verbs join with other verbs to help form different tenses.*

Auxiliary	Auxiliary and Verb
have be will	I **have** *seen* lion tracks around the camp. Don't bother me. I **am** *eating* my dinner. I **will be** *finishing* soon.
may do	You **may** *become* dinner if you don't listen to me. I **do** not *think* that is funny.

1. Identify the "**helper**" (**auxiliary**) verbs for each of the tenses.

(a) Which two tenses do not need a helper verb? _____

(b) Which "helper verbs" are commonly used with the present continuous?

_____

(c) What do all the continuous verbs have in common? (Hint — look at the main verb.)

_____

(d) Which "helpers" are used with the present perfect? _____

_____

(e) Which are commonly used with the past continuous? _____

_____

(f) Which "helper" can you find for the past perfect? _____

_____

(g) Is there anything special about the simple future tense? _____

_____

2. Is there anything else that is special about the "helper" (auxiliary) verbs?

_____

Question marks: using auxiliary verbs

- They are going to Scitech on Friday.
- He can do it faster than John.
- You bought a new computer.
- You could have come with us.

Are they going to Scitech on Friday?
Can he do it faster than John?
Did you buy a new computer?
Could you have come with us?

1. Write as many auxiliary verbs as you can think of to start a question.

_____

_____

2. Can you think of the answers to these jokes? Write them on another piece of paper.

(a) Why do kettles whistle?   (c) Where can you find a helping hand?

(b) What is yellow and goes up and down?

Sometimes writers use a question in their writing, but they do not expect the reader to answer it. They do this to draw attention to something they think is important, then they answer the question themselves.

3. There are some examples of this in the following paragraph. Underline them.

> John approached the house. Everything inside appeared dark and deserted, but he could clearly see the tiny pinpoint of light indicating that someone was inside searching. Someone with a flashlight. What should he do now? Should he run back to the beach house and call the police? What if it was too late, by the time the police arrived? He couldn't take a chance. With bated breath he pushed open the heavy front door and tiptoed inside.

*There are times when a question is not really a question — when you tell someone **about** a question someone else has asked.*
She often asks, "What should I do next?" (This is a direct question — it needs a question mark.)
She often asks what she should do next. (This is a reported question — it does not need a question mark.)

4. Change these direct questions to reported questions.

(a) Where are my socks? _____

(b) What is the problem with your bike? _____

_____

Question marks: Questioning activities

1. Read the passage and identify the questions. Add the necessary question marks.

> He often asks his mother if he can go to the movies.
> "Why do you always want to go to the movies" is her constant reply. "Where do you think the money is coming from. Even if we were rich, I would still say no. Are you aware of how much time you waste on TV and watching movies. Your father asked me yesterday how much time you spend studying. Do you realize that you only spend about an hour a week."
> Usually, however, she gives in to him.

2. The following is a nonsense passage. Even if you do not fully understand it, you will be able to write some comprehension questions. Include the answers to your questions.

> The bingy badlup was feeling very froidled because he had not scerded his bongles. Whenever the badlup felt froidled, he wazered to the nearby bunger and rambered sippily with his badret grandlets. The badret's grandlets were not very saller, but the badlup did not care. He was feeling so froiled that he thought anyone who would listen to his raddles was saller and, anyway, it made him feel simpy.

Here are two questions to help you start.

What kind of badlup was he? The badlup was bingy.

How was the badlup feeling? He was feeling very froiled.

(a) _____

_____

(b) _____

_____

(c) _____

_____

(d) _____

_____

(e) _____

_____

3. Can you explain why you were able to answer questions from a passage you could not

fully understand? _____

_____

An exposition is a text in which the writer examines a problem and then gives his or her point of view. Expositions often link causes and actions. Causes go back in time. Actions go forward in time, for example, "Prices were reduced (cause) so shoppers began to rush to the stores again (result)"

1. Read the following exposition.

Underline examples of cause in red. Underline the effects in blue.

Global Warming

Scientists are concerned about the way the climate all over the world has changed. The world has been growing hotter. As a result of this increased temperature, ice in the Arctic Region and the Antarctic Region has been melting rapidly. The snow on mountain tops is receding. Changes have also been happening to plants and wildlife and many animals are now migrating to new areas, as they search for food. The water level is getting higher and this threatens to make some low-lying countries and islands disappear.

What has caused this problem? According to scientists, humans are responsible. In trying to earn money, people have chopped down trees and cleared big areas of land for agriculture. Trees help the Earth's atmosphere because they use up carbon dioxide and change it into oxygen. Carbon dioxide can destroy the atmosphere. When infrared rays from the sun come into the Earth's atmosphere, the atmosphere traps the rays and keeps the Earth warm. Small amounts of carbon dioxide are good because they keep the Earth warm, but if there is too much, the atmosphere will be affected and more rays will come in. Car exhaust fumes and smoke and fumes from industries have put more carbon dioxide into the atmosphere.

Countries that are destroying trees say that they need to make use of their resources or their people will die, but it is possible that there will not be a next generation, if something is not done now. We should reduce the gas emissions from industry by using less fossil fuels like oil and coal. The amount of gas in the air could be reduced by preventing forest fires and logging. We could stop using cars as much and try car pooling, walking, cycling and using public transportation. We could stop using spray cans that produce CFCs.

There are lots of things that we could do to help, but we must start now if we want to prevent mass flooding on Earth.

---

2. Now look at the verb tenses. Explain why they have changed. _____

_____

_____

3. Complete the following cause and effect sentences.

(a) The path was slippery so _____.

(b) He passed his test easily because _____.

(c) He will not be playing tennis today due to _____.

Sentences: conjunctions

Sentences can have more than one clause.
Two separate clauses can be made into one sentence.
You can do this by using a conjunction.
This is just another way of saying "joining word."
In this lesson we are going to discover more about conjunctions.
We are going to explore the way a conjunction can relate two clauses.

1. Read the sentences below.

> Jane likes to drink milk. Jane likes to drink orange juice.

2. Underline the conjunctions in these sentences.

(a)   Jane likes to drink milk and orange juice.

(b)   Jane likes to drink milk, but not orange juice.

(c)   Jane likes to drink either milk or orange juice.

3. Identify the conjunctions in these three sentences. Explain how the conjunction changes the meaning of each sentence.

(a)   You may have jam or butter with your toast. _____

_____

(b)   You may have jam and butter with your toast. _____

_____

(c)   You may have jam, but not butter, with your toast. _____

_____

4. Make up some compound sentences of your own to show how the meaning changes when you change the conjunction.
Use some of the conjunctions shown above.

(a) _____

(b) _____

(c) _____

(d) _____

(e) _____

(f) _____

Compound sentences and conjunctions

The following clauses have been joined to make a
compound sentence using **conjunctions**.

> Alex hates cocoa. He accepted a cup of cocoa from
> Mrs. James. He wanted to be polite.

> Although Alex hates cocoa, he accepted a cup of cocoa
> from Mrs. James because he wanted to be polite.

1. Find the words that join the clauses to make a **compound
sentence** in the sentence above and underline them.

2. Join the clauses below to make **compound sentences**.

(a) Jane visits her Aunt. Jane chooses to go by plane. Jane hates bus travel.

_____

_____

(b) I lived in Indonesia. I could buy many different kinds of fruit. At home I can buy
only oranges and apples.

_____

_____

_____

(c) Rachel does not think meat is good for you. Rachel became a vegetarian.
Rachel wants to live a healthier lifestyle.

_____

_____

_____

(d) Robert's parents are not rich. Robert wants to go to college. He is prepared to
work hard.

_____

_____

_____

3. List the **conjunctions** you used.

Linking to make compound sentences

 Two clauses with the same subject can be joined by a linking word or phrase.

I'm much better at using conjunctions to join clauses. Just test me, James, and you'll see.

Okay, I'll write a clause and a conjunction, then you add the second clause.

1. Georgia completed James' test very successfully. Can you do it too? Compare your answers with students in your class.

(a) Singapore is very close to the equator, therefore, _____

_____

(b) Gravity attracts objects towards the center of the Earth, consequently, _____

_____

(c) The rainforest is being cut down at a very rapid rate, as a result, _____

_____

(d) Mosquitoes can cause diseases, for example, _____

_____

(e) The World Wildlife Fund is trying to protect endangered animals, however, _____

_____

(f) Pollution is very bad for your health, in fact, _____

_____

(g) The Internet is becoming more and more popular, furthermore, _____

_____

(h) I finished the test James set for Georgia, meanwhile, _____

_____

2. What did you notice about the punctuation? _____

_____

Pronouns *are often used in sentences so you do not have to keep repeating the same nouns. They are also used to help you connect ideas.*

Personal pronouns
(refer to persons)
I, me, we, us, you, he, him, she, her, they, them, it

Possessive pronouns
(indicate ownership)
mine, his, hers, ours, yours, theirs

Relative pronouns
(relates two thoughts together)
who, whom, whose, which, that

Reflexive pronouns
(indicate that the subject is also the object)
herself, himself, itself, ourselves, themselves, yourself

Demonstrative pronouns
(used to point to something)
this, that, these, those
(if they are used before a noun they become adjectives)

There are other pronouns, but these are the main ones we use.

Find out what the people are saying below. Add a pronoun. The brackets will tell you which kind of pronoun to add.

Jenny: Give it to _____ (personal). It's _____ (possessive).

Peter: No it's not. It's _____ (possessive). I bought it _____ (reflexive).

Mother: Then _____ (relative) toy is _____ ?(demonstrative)

Peter: Sorry, Jenny. _____ (demonstrative) one is _____

(possessive) and _____ (demonstrative) one is _____ (possessive).

Relative and reflexive pronouns

 Reflexive pronouns *are used when the subject and object of a sentence are the same person.*

"Look, Mom! **The baby** is feeding herself." **The baby** is both the subject and object.	"Oh no! I've cut **myself**." **I** is both the subject and object.	"**My cat** cleans himself." **My cat** is both the subject and object.

1. Write two sentences using reflexive pronouns.

(a) _____

(b) _____

 Relative pronouns are pronouns that are used to introduce adjective clauses. They do two things. They refer to the noun directly in front of them and they join two thoughts (clauses) together. They are similar to conjunctions.

The vase was broken. It was my Grandma's. The vase **that** was broken was my Grandma's.	The girl spoke to me. She is my sister. The girl **who** spoke to me is my sister.	The road is bumpy. It leads to the beach. The road, **which** is bumpy. leads to the beach.

2. On another piece of paper, write two sentences using relative pronouns.

 This seems very simple, however, relative pronouns used for people can be very tricky. First, you need to decide whether the person is the subject or the object of a sentence because a different pronoun is used in each case. Luckily there are some easy rules to help you know which ones to use. They are:

Subject	Object
I, **we**, **she**, **they** and **who** are used in the subject. For example, we write:	**Me**, **us**, **him her**, **them**, and **whom** are used in the object. For example, write to me:
Who is coming?	To **whom** are you writing?
Tom and **I** are friends.	He saw Tom and **me**.
It was **she** who did it.	I saw Jean and **her**.

3. Write two subject sentences and two object sentences.

(a) _____

(b) _____

(c) _____

(d) _____

Relative clauses and relative pronouns

*Earlier you found out you can join two sentences (clauses) to make one sentence. Sometimes, one of the clauses is not as important as the other. When this happens, the more important sentence is called the main clause, and the other sentence is called the **relative clause**. The **relative clause** is usually introduced by a **relative pronoun** and it describes things. It can be the subject or the object of the **relative clause**.*

Look at the sentences in the box below.
The **subject** of the relative clause is in **bold** print.
The *relative pronoun* is in italics.

1. Complete the missing compound sentences.

Main clause	Relative clause	Compound sentence with relative pronoun
I saw the dog.	**The dog** had only one eye.	I saw the dog *which* had only one eye.
Jan has a new niece.	**She** was born last Friday.	Jan has a new niece *who* was born last Friday.
Keiko is my friend.	**She** is coming to visit.	(a) _____
I watched Tam.	**He** is a good diver.	(b) _____

2. Now look at the sentences in the second box.
The object of the relative clause is in bold print and the relative pronoun is in italics.
Complete the missing compound sentences.

Main clause	Relative clause	Compound sentence with relative pronoun
This is my teacher.	You met **her** at assembly.	This is my teacher, *whom* you met at assembly.
John is my pen pal.	I write to **him** every week.	John is my pen pal, to **whom** I write every week
He lent me his bike.	He bought the **bike** last week.	He lent me his bike, *which* he bought last week.
Dimitri owns a horse.	He rode **the horse** yesterday.	(a) _____
I played with the boy.	I bought a game from **him**.	(b) _____

John is my pen pal to whom I write every week.

Did you notice in the second clause the preposition "to" was kept with the relative pronouns "whom"? Although this is a rule in written language, not many people obey it in spoken language. Most people would say, "This is my pen pal John who I write to every week." This rule applies to **which**, but it does not apply to **that**.

For example: I would write **This is the club to which my sister belongs.**

I would not write **This is the club to that my sister belongs.**

Instead I would write **This is the club that my sister belongs to.**

Did you also notice that:

* **who** is used for people, while **which** and **that** are generally used for animals, places and things?

* sometimes, especially when we are talking, we can leave out the relative pronoun without losing any m meaning? For example, instead of saying **"She wore the dress that she bought last year,"** we often say **"She wore the dress she bought last year."**

* relative clauses are usually preceded by a comma?

  Relative pronouns and clauses are quite difficult if you do not know the rules. However, not all of them are. Relative pronouns that show possession are easy, because you only have to remember to use "whose."

1. Complete the compound sentences below.

Look at the car.	It crashed into a tree.	Look at the car that crashed into a tree.
This is the man.	He e-mailed you last week.	This is the man that e-mailed you last week.
There is the cat.	It ruined the curtains.	(a) _____
This is my friend.	He borrowed your bike.	(b) _____ _____
There is the girl.	Her mother is the mayor.	(c) _____ _____

Relative clauses are often inserted into sentences.

2. Look at the sentences below. Make up a rule that tells about when to use commas.

That boy is covered in spots. That boy should go to the doctor immediately.

That boy, who is covered in spots, should go to the doctor immediately.

Ants live in colonies. Ants are insects. **Ants, which are insects, live in colonies.**

_____

_____

Relative clauses *and relative pronouns are often used in science reports.*
The report below was written by a student.

1. Underline the relative clauses and pronouns in the report.

## Snails	
Snails belong to the mollusk family which includes creatures that have soft bodies and protective shells. Other creatures that belong to this family include the octopus, clams, squid and slugs.	⟵ *classification*
The snail is soft-bodied and has a coiled shell which it carries on its back. This shell grows as the snail gets bigger. Its two tentacles, which are situated on its head, have eyes that help it to find its way. If the snail loses an eye, it can grow another.	⟵ *description*
Snails live in dark, damp places where they can hide from predators, such as birds, that like to eat them. The fallen leaves and garden litter, which provide food for the snail, also help to shelter their egg clusters and their young. They come out of hiding in the early morning and late at night to hunt for food because this is the safest time for them.	⟵ *location*
Snails don't have much protection other than their shell. If a snail is attacked or upset, it will pull in its eyes, tentacles and foot and pretend to be dead. It cannot run from its enemies. The large muscular foot, on which it moves, produces a slimy substance called mucus. This mucus helps the snail to glide smoothly over rough surfaces, as well as helping it to stick to smooth surfaces, like glass. Even though the mucus helps them to move, snails are very slow. Snails breathe through a hole which is located under their shells.	⟵ *behavior*
Snails are pests because they destroy young seedlings. Gardeners, who want to protect their plants, usually sprinkle snail pellets around their gardens. French people have another use for them. They call them escargots and cook them in a sauce and serve them in restaurants.	⟵ *ending*

(title is marked at the top of the box with ⟵ title)

2. **(a)** What main tense has the author used? _____

(b) Reports always use specialized terms (words). Write the words that you think are special to the subject of "snails."

_____

_____

(c) Write adjectives used by the author. _____

_____

_____

3. On another piece of paper, write a science report of your own. Check how many relative clauses and pronouns you use.

Activities using relative pronouns and clauses

1. Circle the correct relative pronoun to use.

(a)   The mad dog chased Jessie and (she, her) across the school ground.

(b)   To (whom, who) was the teacher speaking when she raised her voice?

(c)   (Who, whom) left that mess? It was (her, she) who did it.

(d)   You may come with James and (I, me).

2. Use who, whose or whom to complete these sentences.

(a)   The friends _____ I knew in kindergarten are still my best friends.

(b)   The man _____ car is always parked outside, owns the store.

(c)   The boy from _____ I bought the game, lives next door.

(d)   The friend with _____ I was traveling had an accident in Spain.

(e)   This book is owned by _____?

(f)   The girl _____ I saw, told me to come back later.

3. Finish these sentences by completing the relative clause.

(a)   The teacher rewarded the girl who

_____.

(b)   The girl who _____ showed us how to do it.

(c)   Mr. Brown, who _____ isn't very nice.

(d)   The dog, to which _____ is black and tan.

(e)   The lady whose _____ was very embarrassed.

(f)   We haven't finished with the books which

_____.

(g)   The house that _____ isn't finished yet.

(h)   The clothes which _____ were very dirty.

(i)   The girl to whom _____ was very polite.

Grammar through persuasive text — 1

The Seventh Grade students at Brown School are very unhappy. The principal, Mr. Smith, canceled the Seventh Grade social because three students from Seventh Grade had misbehaved. The students on the Seventh Grade Student Council decided to write to the Principal.

May 23, 1999

Mr. Smith, Principal
Brown School
325 Main St.
Boston, MA

Dear Mr. Smith,

The Seventh Grade students have asked us to write to you about the announcement you made at our last assembly regarding our end of semester social.

We feel very strongly that canceling the Seventh Grade end of semester social because of the behavior of three students is very unfair. By canceling the social you are also punishing the rest of the students, who are honest and diligent.

As you know, Seventh Grade Council has worked hard to organize and promote this social. Six parents also have been very busy helping us to raise funds. We feel that our special efforts have not been considered in your decision.

In addition, Samantha's brothers' band has generously offered to play for free at the social. It will be embarrassing to have to tell them the social is canceled, as we know they have had to turn down a paid request so they could keep their promise to us.

Instead of canceling our social, would it be possible to appropriately discipline the three students involved? This would be fairer to those who have not done anything wrong.
Thank you for considering our request.

Sincerely,

Amanda

Council President

1. Why do you think the students decided to write to Mr. Smith?

(a) _____

(b) _____

2. What do they want Mr. Smith to do?

(a) _____

_____

(b) _____

_____

Grammar through persuasive text — 2

1. Do you think Amanda has presented a strong argument in her letter to Mr. Smith? _____

2. Is her letter persuasive? _____

3. Is her letter polite? _____

4. Does she express clearly what the students want Mr. Smith to do? _____

Amanda used a special structure to help her write a letter to Mr. Smith. This helped her to organize her thoughts, so her argument would be persuasive. This is the structure she used.

Dear Mr. Smith,

The Seventh Grade students have asked us to write to you about the announcement you made at our last assembly, regarding our end of semester social. ← *Purpose of the letter*

We feel very strongly that canceling the Seventh Grade end of semester social because of the behavior of three students is very unfair. By canceling the social you are also punishing the rest of the students, who are honest and diligent. ← *Thesis or opinion*

As you know, the Seventh Grade Council has worked hard to organize and promote this social. Six parents also have been very busy helping us to raise funds. We feel that our special efforts have not been considered in your decision. ← *Argument and support for the argument*

In addition, Samantha's brothers' band has generously offered to play for free at the social. It will be embarrassing to have to tell them the social is canceled, as we know they have had to turn down a paid request so they could keep their promise to us. ← *Argument and support for the argument*

Instead of canceling our social, would it be possible to appropriately discipline the three students involved? This would be fairer to those who have not done anything wrong. ← *Suggestion for action*

Thank you for considering our request. ← *Polite conclusion*

5. Look at the verbs used in the letter.

(a) What verb tense is used the most? _____

(b) Why do you think this tense is used? _____

_____

(c) Explain why the tense changes in some places. _____

_____

(d) Underline each auxiliary (helper verb) in the letter. Hint: you may find the verb "to be" (i.e., am, is, are, was, were, be, being, been) and the verb "to have" (i.e., have, has, had).

(e) Amanda used emotive language — language which helps to arouse feelings.
Draw a circle around words (or phrases) you think are examples of emotive language.

Changing words into different parts of speech

The word "poison" is a noun. It can be changed into an adjective by adding a suffix that means "full of."

1. Look at the cartoons below and fill in the blanks.

(a) He is full of nerves.

He is _____

(b) It is full of danger.

It is _____

(c) She is full of glamour.

She is _____

2. The words "happy" and "legal" are adjectives.
They can be changed into adverbs by using a suffix. What is the suffix? _____

3. Complete the sentences below.

(a) It needs immediate action.

He should do it
_____.

(b) They want a peaceful solution.

They want to settle it
_____.

(c) She should proceed with caution.

Ooohhh...

She had better move
_____.

4. There are lots of ways we can change a verb into the name of a person who does the action that is indicated by the verb. Write the name of the person who does the following and the suffix you have used.

(a) A person who teaches is a _____, _____

(b) A person who acts is an _____, _____

(c) A person who works in politics _____, _____

(d) A person who types is a _____, _____

(e) One who works is a _____, _____

(f) One who does accounts is an _____, _____

(g) One who resides there is a _____, _____

5. Find other occupations that use these suffixes. Write them on another piece of paper.

Teachers Notes and Answers

Using verb tenses

Page 8: the past perfect
Question 2: (a) had put (b) had marked (c) had escaped (d) had completed (e) had said (f) had swept

Question 3: When we write **direct speech** we write the actual words the speaker says. The words are placed within quotation marks. When we tell someone else what the person said, we don't use quotation marks because it is **indirect (reported) speech.** If the action is **still happening,** the tense doesn't change, e.g., "I am tired!" becomes "He said that he is tired." The tense is present in both cases. If the reported speech is a **truth statement,** the tense doesn't change, e.g., "Lions belong to the cat family," becomes "The teacher said that lions belong to the cat family."

If the introductory verb is **in the present or future tense,** the tense doesn't change, e.g., She says, "He is very handsome," becomes "She says that he is very handsome." The tense needs to change if the indirect statement refers to the past. In this case we need to change the time, place and pronouns.

Page 9: More about the past perfect tense
Answers will vary.

Using Punctuation

Page 10: review
Questions 1 and 2: Punctuation is used to assist the reader to read text the way the writer intended.

Question 3: exclamation mark, apostrophe, quotation marks, period, capital letter, comma, question mark, parenthesis, dash, hyphen, semicolon, colon.

Question 4: (a) question mark (b) period (c) semicolon or comma (d) A period shows the end of a sentence. It is also used for abbreviations (e) commas (f) quotation marks (g) capital letter (h) exclamation mark (i) possessive apostrophe (j) exclamation mark (k) apostrophe.

Question 5: Answers will vary.

Question 6: quotation marks, question mark, periods, apostrophes

Page 11: Commas, dashes and parentheses
Question 2: Answers will vary.
The following guidelines may be useful:
use dashes if the extra information:
- explains, emphasizes or repeats an idea that comes before it in the sentence, e.g., It was rumored that the old lady had a secret hoard of money — money she had stolen a long time ago.
- indicates interruptions or breaks in speech, e.g., "He — he — he took my chocolate," sobbed the small boy.
- indicates a list of nouns belongs to a group, e.g., She bought balloons, party hats, whistles and bags of candy — all for the birthday party.

Use parentheses if the extra information:
- doesn't fit into the flow of the sentence, e.g., She joined the basketball team (even though she disliked sports)

because her best friend wanted her to play.
- when the writer seems to be adding something personal, e.g., I get the feeling (I don't know why) that they are not really convinced we are serious.
- when you are giving dates in a biography, e.g., Isaac Newton (1645–1727) was one of the greatest inventors who ever lived.

Use commas if the extra information:
- is an added phrase, e.g., General Solo, of the first regiment, inspected the troops.
- is an added clause, e.g., General Solo, the first man to graduate from the academy, inspected the new recruits.

Page 12: More about parenthetical expressions
Questions 1 and 2: Answers will vary.

Question 3: Use the information given for page 11 to help answer the students' responses.

Using words

Page 13: homophones
Question 1: Ensure that students know the difference between a homophone and a homograph by explaining that "**homo**" means "same," "**graphien**" means "to write" and "**phone**" means "sound." Thus, homophone means **same sound** (but different spelling and meaning, e.g., their, there, they're) while homograph means the same spelling, but different meaning, e.g., "I will **park** the car here, so you can play in the **park**."

Question 2: (a) great, board (b) serial (c) herd (d) Principal, current (e) stationary (f) piece, bread (g) die, bury (h) scene (i) rote

Questions 3 and 4: Answers will vary. Have students attempt the activity before consulting a dictionary. Accept definitions from any dictionary.

Making use of words

Page 14: linking words
Question 2: Accept phrases and clauses if students have included them. However, the stress is on linking words in time: last week, at 10 o'clock, when we arrived, first, during, after that, later on, before we moved, finally, in plenty of time to …, the next day.

Question 3: our, we (each time it occurs), I (each time it occurs), it, this.

Question 4: Accept phrases and clauses, but the emphasis is on the following linking adverbs: because, when, but, although, when, where, as well as, however.

Page 15: Sentence structure
Questions 1 – 4: Answers will vary.
Before introducing activity 4, review the structure of writing directions. Emphasize that instructions in directions can begin with either action verbs (imperative forms) or sequence markers such as first, next, then, after, and before.

Teachers Notes and Answers

Sentences

Page 16: clauses

Question 1: Answers will vary.

After students have read the narrative, discuss the "did you know" entry. Have them identify clauses in two or three sentences and report their findings orally, before requiring them to complete the activities that follow.

Possible answers are: (a) enjoys, practices, 2 clauses (b) wrote, 1 clause (c) closed, went, 2 clauses.

Question 3: It was solid and roomy; Dad said it was…; He returned a few minutes later…; The children laughed; Dad was right; Now they had a real home of their own …

Page 17: Sentences that have more than one clause

Question 1: Dad was recruited to help (C1) timber was located (C2) tools and ropes borrowed (C3) nails acquired from Dad's collection in the shed (C4).

Question 2: Explain that sometimes it reads more clearly to leave was and were in some of the clauses. They do not need to omit all of them. Discuss the students' answers by asking them to justify deletions.

Page 18: Identifying components of a clause

Question 1: (a) The children (b) set (c) to work happily.

Question 2: This question may cause some debate because the situation part of the sentence has been split in two. Allow the students to try the activity before informing them of the answer.

No. 2 naming part 3 action part 1 + 4 situation part

Question 3: (a) either Carefully the dentist drilled, or The dentist carefully drilled (b) either The crocodile quietly or slid into the water quietly. (c) either Impatiently Justine waited or for the bus impatiently. (d) either Powerfully Kieran swam or through the water powerfully.

Page 19: Changing the order of sentences

Question 1: (b) The towering mountain range (N) loomed (A) gloomy and forbidding, over the village (S).
(c) The scouts (N) folded (A) their tents without any … (S).
(d) The house next to the big park (N) is (A) Robert's house (S).
(e) The football game (N) was postponed (A) because of the cyclone (S).
(f) The car (N) was stopped (A) by the police because the driver was speeding (S).
(g) The moon (N) crept (A) silently and softly across the dark, dark sky (S).

For the second part of the exercise, have students experiment with shifting the sentence parts around. If the object has two situation parts, discuss how these could be split and moved.

Question 2: How (silently and softly) where (across the dark, dark sky)

Question 3: (a) how (gloomy and forbidding) where (over the village) (b) what (is Robert's house) (c) when (as they marched past the officer) (d) why (because of the cyclone).

Clause structure

Page 20: the subject (noun groups)

Questions 1 and 2: Answers will vary. Discuss the noun

groups and complete the activity orally before students record their preferences and share these with the class.

Page 21: More about noun groups

Question 1: Compare answers given by students. Write a random list on the board. Orally categorize the nouns in preparation for the activity on page 22.

Question 2: elephant, hippo, giraffe and water buffalo.

Question 3: sheep, birds (general), pigeons, geese

Clause Components

Page 22: nouns

Question 1: Discuss the random list compiled from page 21. Have students complete and compare their answers. Mark by completing the page with the students using an overhead projector sheet.

Question 2: hippos (plural, countable) cow (feminine, singular, countable) flock (singular, countable) water (uncountable) lion (singular, countable) uncle (masculine, singular, countable).

Clause structure

Page 23: verbs (action part)

Answers to all sections will vary. Compare and discuss students' responses.

Page 24: verbs

Question 1: am (I'm) looking, is, was, used, left, was calling, ran

Question 2: Part of a word (I'm). Groups of words (am looking, was calling). Action already happened (was, used, left, was calling, ran). Have –ing at the end (looking, calling).

Question 3: (a) arrived, lifted, (b) is, are, annoy (c) alters, repairs, designs (d) am going, will pick (e) will be, can meet

Question 4: Action has already happened (arrived, lifted) action is in the present (is, are, annoy, alters, repairs, designs) action will happen in the future (am going, will pick, will be, can meet)

Words

Page 25: using interesting verbs

Questions 1, 2 and 4: Answers will vary. Brainstorm, discuss and make a chart of student discoveries.

Question 3: (a) looked (b) nudged (c) writhe (d) dragged (e) drenched (f) stopped (g) lived (h) found (i) said (j) lessen

Clause structure

Page 26: the object (situation part)

Question 2: They tell us the reason for the action.

Question 3: (a) because he would fall over (adverbial clause of reason tells why) if he lifted the other one (adverbial clause of reason tells why) (b) in the days of knights (adverbial phrase of time tells when) (c) in one ear and out the other (adverbial phrase of place tells where) (d) at the back of the clock shop (adverbial phrase of place tells where) (e) the piano (noun phrase which is the object of the verb play tells what) very (adverb of degree tells how much) loudly (adverb of manner tells how) until I found the right key (adverbial clause of time tells when).

Situation components

Page 27: adverbial phrases

Question 1: It depends on the circumstance, for example, in an emergency situation such as an accident, you would use the word "immediately" rather than the phrase "as soon as possible" of you are issuing instructions. In a story, you might use the adverbial phrase "as soon as possible" if you are issuing instructions. In a story, you might use the adverbial phrases to paint a more vivid word picture for your readers.

Question 2: (a) The children ran across the park when mother called. Type: time (b) Pete studies very hard every night. Type: degree and frequency (c) The mountaineer climbed very carefully down the steep incline. Type: manner and place. (d) The apple pie was very, very hot. Type: degree. (e) The girl swam expertly through the surf. Type: manner and place. (f) The old man and woman lived in a cottage in the woods. Type, place. The soprano sang sweetly at the new concert hall. Type: manner and place.

Question 3: Answers will vary. State a phrase type and ask individual students to read aloud their sentence that matches that phrase type.

Verb Tenses

Page 28: Making sense of verb tenses

Question 1: (a) past, present, future (b) present, future, past

Question 2: (a) She runs fast, She ran fast, She will run fast (b) He reads a book, He read a book, He will read a book (c) She rides her bike, She rode her bike, She will ride her bike.

Using verb tenses in reports

Page 29: the present

Question 1: Paragraph 1: are, are, live, come, is, is, is, is, is, exercise, live, have, exercising, is. Paragraph 2: comes. Paragraph 3: has, shows, is, are, will not get, are walking, can be adjusted, can make, go, varies, is, is, allow, decide, will take, forgets, switches, is, is, ensure, run, leave, stops. Paragraph 4: is, don't have, live, is, don't have, should buy, are, lives.

For more able students, you may wish to introduce the continuous form (are walking) and model auxiliaries (will, be, can, should, do).

Question 2: A report about a machine.

Question 3: The order is: title, classification, description, dynamics, summary comment/use.

Verb Tenses

Page 30: the present tense

Question 1: It tells you about a process or an action that is taking place right now. If students are already familiar with present tenses you may wish to introduce simple, continuous and perfect forms of present tense.

Questions 2 and 3: Answers will vary.

Page 31: Writing present (simple) sentences

Question 1: (a) to talk about habits (b) to talk about facts that have been the same for a long time (c) to express facts that are known to be true.

Questions 2 – 4: Answers will vary.

Page 32: Using adverbs with present (simple) tense

Question 1: Answers will vary.

Question 2: (a) everywhere (where) often (frequency) wildly (how); (b) gently (how), sometimes (frequency), loudly (how); (c) near (where), angrily (how); regularly (frequency), occasionally (frequency); (d) soon (when) seldom (frequency), close to (where); (e) barely (degree), easily (how); (f) always (frequency), later (when), madly (how) there (where), before (when).

Page 33: the past tense

Answers will vary. Have students share their responses with the class. If students are advanced, introduce other forms of past tense such as past continuous and past perfect.

Page 34: Past tense in narratives —1

Question 1: Most stories are written about events that have already happened.

Question 2: was, lived, was, was admired, had tried, to persuade, to travel, to become, to be, to own, was sent, refused, persuaded, weighing down, were returned, became, shouted (past tense), am, dare, deny, are, find, is, desires, (present tense because they are direct speech).

Question 4: Direct speech in narratives reflects what is being said at that present time, so it is written in present tense.

Page 35: Past tense in narratives — 2

Question 1: Janet **was** feeling sick. She **coughed** painfully and **tried** hard to cover her mouth as she **did** so, but with each cough, she **felt** weaker. She **wanted** to lift her head from the pillow, but it **felt** heavy and laden. Her head **turned** slowly to peer through the window next to her bed. Her **eyes fixed** on the watery patterns that **formed** on the glass and she **was** unsure of whether the patterns really **existed,** or whether they **were caused** by the unwelcome tears that constantly **formed** in her eyes. Across the road she saw the distorted shapes of her friends who **played** happily in the puddles. They **splashed** water and mud at each other and **squealed** with delight. "It's not fair," she thought. "I want to go out there and play too. Why did I have to catch the flu?" Draw attention to the fact that direct speech remains in the present tense.

Page 36: talking about the future — 1

Answers to the activity will vary.

Page 37: talking about the future – 2

Questions 1 and 2: Answers may vary.

Some possible answers to question 2 include: (a) cartoonist (b) teacher, mother, pediatrician (c) equestrian, jockey, farmer (d) carpenter, cabinet maker, builder, architect (e) scientist, teacher, accountant (f) chef, restaurant owner (g) doctor, lawyer, teacher, lecturer, (any professional occupation) (h) travel agent, pilot – any occupation involving travel (i) doctor, nurse.

Direct and Reported Speech

Page 38: Direct and reported speech – 1

Question 1: (a) David said that he is really, really tired.

(b) Dad said that he knows I can do it. (c) The teacher said it's not polite to push in the line. (d) Rick said he's going to the beach. (e) Jackie said she has a new computer game.

Question 2: (a) No (b) Yes. The pronouns had to change because they are no longer first person reporting. They have to change to third person. Sometimes the verb changes also to match the pronoun, e.g., I have becomes he has, I am becomes he is.

Page 39: Direct and reported speech — 2

Question 1: (a) Dylan said that the movie is very boring and he doesn't think I'd like it. I told him that I still want to see it because everyone else in my class has seen it.
(b) Jenny informed the class that snakes are reptiles because they are coldblooded. Nancy asked if that is why they are very slow moving in winter.

Page 40: Direct and reported speech — 3

Question 1: (a) James said he's really hungry. He wants to go to the coffee store to buy a donut. (b) Janet replied that she's hungry too, but she doesn't like donuts.
(c) Answers will vary.
The Queen's adviser said that the earth is flat. He said that Christopher Columbus is a fool. Christopher Columbus replied that the earth is round. He can prove it, if the Queen lets him have a ship and crew.

Question 2: Answers will vary. Collate the students' responses and make a class chart. Add to the chart whenever a student discovers a new word for "said."

Page 41: Direct and reported speech — 4

Question 1: Tom's dialogue that contains speech marks.

Question 2: (a) past tense (b) present tense

Question 3: We were talking about the different ways animals move and he said he knows and animal that has 50 legs, but it can't walk. She said to Jack he should tell the class about it. Well, Jack stood up and said the creature he is thinking of is a centipede that's been cut in half.

Question 4: The tense stays the same when someone is reporting the direct speech of another person.

Question 5: Answers will vary.

Page 42: tense changes

Question 1: Reported speech: they heard Harvey's quacking… Direct speech: "We weren't sure about having a duck as a guard dog."

Question 2: (a) Neighbors said, "We heard Harvey's quacking and contacted the home owners…"

Question 3: Mr. Henderson said he wouldn't swap Harvey for the world and that he was a real hero.

Question 5: (a) He explained, "I never eat seafood." (b) He said, "I'm waiting for the bus."

Page 43: quotation marks

Question 1: Students should underline any speech that is enclosed by quotation marks.

Question 2: (a) The title of the cookbook (b) for popular quotations, e.g. "Let your fingers do the walking."
You may also wish to point out that quotation marks can be used for quotations within quotations. In this case, single quotation marks are used; for example, "The movie I saw with you last week, was 'The Borrowers' I think," said Jane.

Quotation marks are used also in sentences to enclose the meanings of words: for example, I always thought the word "hibernate" only applies to animals until I met my friend John, who hated to get out of bed in winter.

Conditionals

Page 44: Making sense of conditionals

Question 1: present tense.

Question 2: Answers will vary. Use the classification given in the examples to encourage students to offer oral responses before completing the written activity independently.

Page 45: the first condition

Question 1: simple present tense

Question 2: simple future tense (b) you will – you'll (c) they will – they'll (d) she will – she'll (e) I will – I'll (f) he will – he'll

Question 3: Answers will vary.

Page 46: the second condition

Question 1: (a) If I **won** the lottery (b) If you **bought** a lot of tickets (c) If you **had come** to the store with me (d) If I **were** you

Questions 2 and 3: Answers will vary.

Page 47: the third condition

Question 1: Answers will vary.

Question 2: hadn't been (had not been) talking, hadn't seen, had valued.

Question 3: Yes

Question 4: No

Question 5: Answers will vary.

Page 48: Using conditionals in expositions

Question 1: The following should be underlined: (a) if garbage doesn't break down quickly (b) If we can't dispose of them, then (c) If I were a politician (d) … if we don't begin seriously recycling our rubbish (e) If global warming increases (f) … because if we don't, vegetation… (g) If people had started recycling their garbage…

Question 2: The answers to 1 above have been classified. Students could use any of the following: General condition – (a) (b) (e) (f). First condition – (d). Second condition – (c). Third condition – (g). You may want to point out, or have students discover, that the general condition is used the most in expositions, because an exposition should be based on facts.

Describing characters

Page 49: using adjectives

Question 1: An adjective is a describing word.

Question 2: It adds meaning to a noun or pronoun and helps to build up a word picture in the reader's mind.

Question 4: tall, straight, evil, black, bushy, straight, red, (sly and untrustworthy are adverbs of manner in this sentence), black, white, dark, billowing, pale, white, thin, normal, long, dank, black, dirty, sharp, white, ugly, permanent, stubby, piercing. You may also wish to draw attention to Scott's use of similes (like a count, a bit like a pixie).

Page 50: tenses

Question 1: Fictional writing; past tense

Question 3: Reports are written mostly in present tense and narratives are written mostly in past tense.

Question 4: Accept any logical answers. Narrative adjectives are more varied and are used to evoke mood through description, while adjectives in reports are confined to describing scientific features and are more factual.

Question 5: They are adverbs of manner.

Question 6: Accept any logical answers – however, stress that some students over-use adjectives and it detracts from their work.

Question 8: Accept any improvements to the sentences. Have students decide which is the best combination of adjectives for the nouns in the sentences.

Page 51: metaphor

Question 2: (a) a shimmering blanket (b) a clear, blue ceiling (c) a lamp on high (d) paddles of steel

Question 3: Answers will vary.

Complete a concept map of the students' responses on the chalkboard and write a class poem. Have students choose metaphors from the concept map and then write an individual poem.

Page 52: similes

Question 1: Similes compare two things or actions. A simile is usually introduced using the words **like** or **as**. Metaphors, on the other hand, identify one object or action with another. Metaphors state that the two things are the same.

Question 2: (a) like a cork (b) like a mermaid (c) like a mountain (d) as fast as a steam train (e) like a seal

Question 3: Answers will vary.

Make charts showing the students' responses.

Making sense of words

Page 53: idioms — 1

Question 1: An idiom is a special saying that is used by speakers who are native to a region. Idioms do not mean what they appear to say.

Question 2: Discuss the pictures and meanings of the idioms (a) in the limelight – likes to star, get attention (b) quite a ham – he overacts (c) mad as a hatter – refers to the Mad Hatter in Alice in Wonderland (d) brings home the bacon – helps the person make money so they can buy food (e) full of beans – energetic like Mexican jumping beans

Question 3: Carefully chosen idioms can make writing more interesting but it is good practice to use them sparingly, and not to use idioms in expository texts. Authors choose to use idioms to make their characters and settings seem genuine and believable.

Page 54: idioms —2

Questions 1 and 2: (c) is different because it is a simile.

Question 3 and 4: Answers will vary.

Grammar

Page 55: newspaper articles

Question 1: Procedure (instructions), report, exposition, recount, explanation, narrative.

Question 2: (a) verb tense — show when an action has taken place (b) point of view — refers to the person who is speaking, or is being spoken about, or is being spoken to (c) vocabulary — a collection of words (d) paragraphing — a grouping of sentences that develops one particular point (e) indirect/direct speech – indicates whether the words were those of a speaker or of a witness (f) linking words – words that connect one sentence or idea to another (g) objectivity — not based on thoughts and feelings.

Question 3: (a) headline — the title of an article (b) byline — writer's name and where the news originated (c) lead — an introduction that may tell who, what, where, when, why and how (d) next most important information — supporting details and facts (e) conclusion — some consequences and future leads.

Page 56: identifying point of view — 1

Question 2: she, he, he, she, I, we, our, their, I, their, he, we, his, us, him

Question 3: I, we, our, us

Questions 4 and 5: Answers will vary.

Page 57: identifying point of view — 2

Question 1: Answers will vary.

Accept any answer that students can justify; e.g., the student may suggest that statement (b) is possible because it could be direct speech given by a bystander and statement (c) could be part of an opinion letter to the editor.

Question 2: (a) (d) (f)

Question 3: (a) he (d) his, he, him (f) him

Question 4: Accept all variations that correctly identify the third person. Possible answers: (b) The accident could have been avoided if the man had checked his equipment before climbing the ladder (or it could be written in the passive, e.g., It was thought that…) (c) The report on the behavior of students made her very angry. She thought that the newspaper should stick to facts when they publish reports. (e) He was advised to relax more and go to the movies this weekend to enjoy a good film.

Page 58: Using active and passive voice

Question 1: (a) Steven (b) vase (c) Dad (d) car

Question 2: broke, washed

Question 3: Answers will vary. At this stage just give an example of the two sentences using passive voice, e.g., (a) "The vase was broken by Steven" and (b) "The car was washed by Dad" so that students can have a basic understanding of the difference between the active and passive voices.

Page 59: More about active voice

Question 1: (a) – (f) should reflect pictures shown. Explain that an easy way to write active sentences such as

Teachers Notes and Answers

John washed the car; is to write the verb (washed) first. Next ask "Who/What?" after the verb (John washed who/what?). The car will be the object. Ensure the subjects are named first because these are active sentences.

Questions 2 – 5: Answers will vary. Mark some student responses aloud by modeling the above procedure.

Page 60: More about passive voice
Question 1: (a) and (b) explain we can tell these sentences are written in passive voice because the "doer of the action" is not known — the answer to who/what comes after the verb. (d), (g) are both passive because the "receiver" is mentioned before the "doer." The 7:30 train is the "doer" because it hit the car; John was the "doer" because he wrote the poem.
Question 2: They all have auxiliary (helper) verbs.

Page 61: Making nouns from other parts of speech
Question 1: celebration, disappearance, impertinence, freedom, hospitality, kingdom, vandalism, kingdom, tourism, recognition, heroism, cooperation, description, direction, action, severity.
Question 2: Celebration — celebrate — verb to a noun; disappearance — disappear — verb to a noun; impertinence — impertinent — adjective to a noun; freedom — free — adjective to a noun; hospitality — hospitable — adjective to a noun; kingdom — king — noun (place) to noun (person); vandalism — vandal — noun (act) to noun (person); tourism — tour — verb or noun to a noun (act); cooperation — cooperate — verb to a noun; severity — severe — adjective to a noun.
Question 3: (a) criticism (b) adoption (c) attraction (d) resistance (e) equality (f) correction (g) collection (h) annoyance (i) residence (j) boredom

Page 62: Newspaper headlines
Question 1: (b) Eagles Fly Home against the Hawks — the Eagles football team defeated a team called the Hawks. (e) Man Bites Dog — story about a visitor from a small village in Malaysia, who had traveled to the US and was tasting hotdogs for the first time. (j) Record Smashed by Window — an athlete with the surname of Window broke a record convincingly.
Question 2: (c), (g), (h) and (j) are past tense; the rest are present tense.
Questions 3 – 5: Answers will vary.

Page 63: Exploring news articles
Question 2: Answers will vary.
Question 3: There are only two passive sentences in this article – (1) The giant's hen … was stolen … while the giant … (2) Bail was refused and Jack was taken to prison.
Question 4: Vandalism, security, kingdom, performance, transportation, vandalism, tolerance, pacifist, action, criticism, population, security, incidence.
Question 5: (a) present tense (b) and (c) Answers will vary. (d) Students need only to recognize past and present forms at this stage; however, some may be able to recognise continuous forms as well. Lodged (past) is noted (present perfect) lashed (past) lays (present) was stolen

(past perfect) was listening (present continuous) was dozing (past continuous) woke (past) saw (past) steal (present) chopped (past) tests (present) stopped (past) want (present) get (past) reacted (past) would be tightened (future perfect) avoid (present) was refused (past perfect) was taken (past perfect).
Have students investigate tense. They need to discover that present tense is used when direct speech is quoted, because the person being quoted is talking about the present. Present tense is also used to report facts that still hold true today.

Verb tenses

Page 64: using verb tenses
Question 1: (a) time (b) when (c) past, present and future
Question 2: Answers will vary.

Page 65: making sense of perfect tense
Question 1: Answers will vary — follow the given pattern and explain that the perfect form tells us whether the action is completed (present perfect), was completed (past) or will be completed (future). Explain that perfect tenses use an auxiliary and a past participle to form the verb. For example, she *has* baked a pie (present perfect); She *will have* baked a pie by the time I get home (future perfect).

Page 66: the present continuous
Answers will vary. Explain that present continuous refers to actions that are taking place right now, even if the actions are not being performed right now while the person is speaking. It is also used to plan activities for the future.

Page 67: past continuous — 1
Question 1: Answers will vary. Refer students to the explanation in the text.
Question 2: (a) was drinking (b) was, looking (c) were chirping (singing, or any alternative), were buzzing (humming) (d) was looking (searching).

Page 68: past continuous — 2
Answers will vary. Refer to the explanation on page 66.

Page 69: future continuous — 1
Answers will vary. Remind students that future continuous is used for actions that will be going on at a time in the future (I will be sleeping by the time you arrive home).

Page 70: future continuous — 2
Answers will vary.

Page 71: Identifying verb tenses — 1
Requires reading only in preparation for the activity on page 72.

Page 72: Identifying verb tenses — 2
Question 1: am writing (present continuous), have planned (present perfect), were learning (past continuous), suggested (past simple), raise (present simple), planned (past simple), are living (present continuous), learned (past simple), had never attended (past perfect), were (past simple), have been fundraising (past continuous), plan (present simple), are (present simple), has joined (present perfect), receive (present

simple), will have raised (future perfect), want (present simple), will appear (future simple), has raised (present perfect), am asking (present continuous), will be aware (future simple).
Question 2: (a) goal keeper *leaped* (b) when I *bit* (c) *was* listening (d) by the time the game *started*. (e) when I *have* finished (f) We have beaten that team every time we *have* played them.

Auxiliaries
Page 73: identifying "helper" verbs
Question 1: (a) simple present and simple past tense (b) am, is, are (c) the main verb ends in –ing because it is a present participle, e.g., am swimming — present continuous; was swimming — past continuous; will be swimming — future continuous; i.e., only the auxiliary verb (helper) changes. (d) has, have (e) was, were (f) had (g) the auxiliaries are usually shall or will. There is also an "is going to" form, for things that are certain to happen.
Question 2: (a) They often are used as a contraction after a pronoun; e.g. he is = he's. They can also be contracted with the words here and there, there is = there's.
(b) When you answer a question that requires a yes or no answer, you usually add the auxiliary to your answer; e.g., Is he coming with us? Yes, he is!
(c) Sometimes they are used in questions, e.g. , That isn't your cat, is it?
Accept any logical observation that students make.

Question marks
Page 74: using auxiliary verbs
Question 1: is, are, was, were, can, may, has, have, had, shall, will, do, did, does, should, could.
Question 2: Have students discover that statements can be turned into questions by changing the order of words. There are certain words that are known as question or "Wh" words — who, whom, whose, which, where, when, what, why. There is also how. Practice using question marks by compiling a student joke book that uses question words such as those in the example. Answers to the jokes (a) because they cannot sing (b) a lemon in an elevator (c) on the end of your arm
Question 3: Questions are marked with a question mark — explain that particular questions are called rhetorical questions, because the writer does not require an answer.
Question 4: When questions are turned into indirect speech, you need to make changes to tenses, pronouns, possessive adjectives and adverbs (time and place).
(a) She asked me to see where her socks were. (b) He asked me what was the problem with my bike.
Page 75: questioning activities
Answers will vary. Accept all reasonable explanations.

Writing expositions
Page 76: shifts in tenses
Question 1: Answers are marked cause (C) and effect (E). Point out that in most cases some form of past tense is used to state causes while some form of present tense is used to state effects. If a cause is stated as a given fact, it

will be written in present tense because it is seen as the present truth that exists right now.
Paragraph 1: scientists are concerned (E) climate has changed (C) has been growing hotter, increased temperature (C), has been melting rapidly, is receding, have also been happening, are now migrating, is getting higher, threatens (E).
Paragraph 2: This entire paragraph is made up of factual information so it is stated in the present tense because it is seen as true at the present time.
Paragraph 3: Note the use of "could" as stating future possibility. You may also wish to point out the use of the conditional in this exposition. Conditional sentences have two parts — an "If–clause" and the main clause. There are three kinds of conditional sentences and each kind has a different pair of tenses for the two clauses. Only the first condition appears in this passage. The first condition referred to probable events. The verb in the "If – clause" is in the present tense (if something is not done, if we want to prevent) and the verb in the main clause is in the future simple tense (There will not be, we could do to help).

Sentences
Page 77: conjunctions
Question 2: (a) and (b) but (c) either/or
Question 3: (a) or (b) and (c) but. In (a) the conjunction means you can have only one of the two (jam or butter). In (b) you can have both jam and butter. In (c) you can only have the one specified (jam).
Question 4: Answers will vary. Have students report their answers and discuss the various conjunctions they have chosen and how each conjunction adds a different meaning to the sentence.
Page 78: Compound sentences and conjunctions
Question 1: although, because
Question 2: Accept any grammatically correct compound sentence that retains the original meaning. (a) Whenever she visits her aunt, Jane chooses to go by plane, because she hates bus travel. Or, since she hates bus travel, Jane chooses to go by plane when she visits her aunt. (b) When I lived in Indonesia, I could buy many different kinds of fruit, but at home I can buy only oranges and apples. (c) Rachael doesn't think meat is good for you, so she became a vegetarian in order to live a healthier lifestyle. (d) If Robert is prepared to work hard, he will be able to go to the university even though his parents are not rich.
Question 3: Answers will vary.
Page 79: Linking to make compound sentences
Question 1: Answers will vary. Have students share selected sentences with class. Discuss the meanings of the new conjunctions and how they relate to the first part of the sentence. Note: "therefore," "consequently" and "as a result" add almost the same meaning to the sentence. Have students suggest other possible conjunctions; for example, "furthermore" could be replaced with "in addition."
Question 2: Draw attention to placement of the semicolon and comma.

Page 80: Types of pronouns

Give it to me. It's mine. No it's not. It's mine. I bought it myself. Then whose toy is this? Sorry, Brian, this one is yours and this/that one is mine.

Page 81: Relative and reflexive pronouns

Answers will vary. Have students share and discuss their sentences with each other.

Page 82: Relative clauses and relative pronouns

Question 1: (a) Keiko is my friend who is coming to visit. Or, Keiko, who is coming to visit, is my friend. (b) I watched Tam who is a good diver.

Question 2: (a) Dimitri owns the horse which/that he rode yesterday (note that the article changes from a horse to the horse — the one Dimitri rode yesterday. Therefore, a definite article is needed. (b) I played with the boy from whom I bought a game.

Page 83: Rules for relative clauses and relative pronouns

Question 1: (a) There is the cat that ruined the curtains. (b) This is my friend **who borrowed your bike.** (c) There is the girl **whose** mother is the mayor.

Question 2: Commas are used between words, phrases and clauses to show the place where extra information has been added to a sentence.

Page 84: Relative clauses in science reports

Question 1: Relative clauses are introduced when the relative pronoun who, which or that is used. (a) which includes creatures that have (b) that belongs to this family (c) coiled shell which it (d) two tentacles, which are (e) birds, that like to eat them, (f) and garden litter, which provide food (g) muscular foot on which it moves (foot is the object so the preposition precedes the relative pronoun), (h) through a hole which is (i) Gardeners who want to protect.

Question 2: (a) present tense (b) possible choices could be: mollusk, soft-bodied, coiled shell, bigger, tentacles, predators, egg clusters, protection, muscular foot, mucus, escargots (c) soft, protective, coiled, dark, damp, garden, early, softest, large, muscular, slimy, rough, smooth, very, slow, young.

Page 85: Activities using relative pronouns and clauses

Question 1: (a) her (b) whom (c) who, she (d) me

Question 2: (a) who (b) whose (c) whom (d) whom (e) whom (f) who

Question 3: Answers will vary.

Page 86: Grammar through persuasive text — 1

Question 1: They want him to change his mind about canceling the social.

Question 2: They want the three students punished in a different way.

Page 87: Grammar through persuasive text — 2

Questions 1 – 4: Answers will vary. Use the questions to trigger discussion. Accept any logical answers that are justified through reference to the text.

Question 5: (a) Mostly in the present tense. (b) Because the letter refers to a current situation that is happening now. (c) The tense changes when the letter refers to past events, e.g., you made, have worked, have been, have not been considered. (d) Students should identify the verb "to be" and the verb "to have" as indicated on the worksheet. (e) Possible answers: feel very strongly, also punishing, honest and diligent, worked hard, busy helping, social efforts, not considered, generously offered, embarrassing, appropriately discipline, fairer, not done anything wrong.

Page 88: Changing words into different parts of speech

Question 1: (a) nervous (b) dangerous (c) glamorous

Question 2: The suffix is –ly — the words are happily and legally (both are adverbs of manner)

Question 3: (a) immediately (b) peacefully (c) cautiously

Question 4: (a) teacher — er (b) actor — or (c) politician — ian (d) typist — ist (e) worker — er (f) accountant — ant (g) resident — ent.

Question 5: Answers will vary.